LARGE PRINT Crosswords

ISBN: 978-1-78599-850-8
AD005275US

Printed in China

2 4 6 8 10 9 7 5 3 1

CONTENTS

1

ACROSS

1 At a snail's pace
5 Surgical procedure
11 "CSI: Miami" network
14 Trig. function
15 Baroque
16 Chop
17 Generally recognized meaning of a word or phrase
19 Battery type, initially
20 Drunken
21 Don't: hyph.
22 Clobber
23 "The ___ of Good Feelings"
25 "Anything ___?"
27 Spinal bone
32 Add to the pot
35 Reverberate
36 Making suitable for upwardly mobile sorts
40 "Aladdin" prince
41 Artsy one
42 "Much ___ About Nothing"
43 County of England
45 A club for Tiger Woods
46 "___ of Duty"
47 Thick-stemmed plant native to tropical America: 2 wds.
49 Exile isle of fame
52 Seek damages
53 Profane oath
56 It's after Shebat
59 Actor's minimum wage
63 Ash cache
64 Extreme or irrational fear of water
66 "Seinfeld" uncle
67 Very early roughly-broken stone implement
68 Amount to make do with
69 "___ & Order"
70 Fought over honor, maybe
71 Codename for the Battle of Normandy: hyph.

DOWN

1 Pierce with a knife
2 Add punch to the punch
3 "___ bitten, twice shy"
4 "…young ambition's ladder, ___ the climber upward turns his face" (Shakespeare's "Julius Caesar")
5 Automated performer of computer tasks
6 Neighbor of Pakistan
7 Not deceived by
8 "Common Sense" pamphleteer
9 Aid in reaching a high shelf, maybe
10 Appetite
11 Blacken
12 Boyfriend
13 Applicator
18 Combustible heap
22 Say it isn't so
24 Bottomless depth
26 Out of harm's way

27 Butcher's offering
28 Acclamation
29 Big African animal, for short
30 Babe or Baby follower
31 Agricultural pest
33 Beauty pageant wear
34 ___ a high note: 2 wds.
37 Andean land
38 Agenda details
39 Departed
41 "My Name Is ___"
44 Chalked sticks
45 Freezing: hyph.
48 President before and after Clinton
50 Louisiana feature
51 Befuddle
53 Select
54 Compound used in fertilizers
55 Winter forecast
57 Husk
58 Automatic
60 Lying, maybe
61 Marge and Homer's middle child
62 "___ Street" ("Annie" song)
64 "If only ___ listened …"
65 Dr.'s degree

2

ACROSS

1 Danish opera composer, August (1859–1939)
5 Award-winning Indian movie star, ___ Kiran
9 City south of Cleveland, Ohio
14 Capital of Rhône
15 Hummus holder
16 São ___, Brazilian city in the state of Minas Gerais
17 Kyle of Tenacious D
18 Time when help is desperately wanted: 3 wds.
20 A pint, maybe
21 eBay attempts
22 Touches with the lips
23 Cramped or squalid room
25 Cutty ___
26 Eye, to Pierre
27 Not straight
31 Ex-senator Sam of Georgia and others
33 Ledger entry
34 Canyon or ranch ending
35 Heroic poem
36 Building managers, slangily
37 Young newts
38 Doubly
39 Largest organ in the human body
40 Duroc domiciles
41 About 39.37 inches: 2 wds.
43 Comparative word
44 Kiln
45 Customary procedure
48 "High ___" (Bogart film)
51 Shed some tears
52 Nickname of Frederick Bean Avery, cartoonist and animator
53 Bound in service
55 "S.O.S.!"
56 Come to mind
57 On or to the left prefix
58 "It was ___ huge mistake!": 2 wds.
59 Like some keys
60 Rare blood type: abbr., 2 wds.
61 Bestselling PC game of the 1990s

DOWN

1 "Enigma Variations" composer
2 African antelope
3 In close opposition: 3 wds.
4 Part of Q & A, briefly
5 Against the odds, as a struggle
6 Electron tube
7 "Look ___ Now, Mother!", Gayle Kirschenbaum movie of 2015: 2 wds.
8 Character voiced by Ossie Davis in Disney's "Dinosaur"
9 To begin with: 2 wds.
10 "An American Rhapsody" star Nastassja
11 Explorer John and performer Charlotte
12 Graceful arch
13 Indicates "yes"
19 Browsing mammals of Central Africa

1	2	3	4		5	6	7	8		9	10	11	12	13
14					15					16				
17					18				19					
20				21					22					
23			24					25						
		26					27					28	29	30
31	32					33						34		
35					36						37			
38				39						40				
41			42						43					
			44					45					46	47
48	49	50					51					52		
53						54					55			
56						57					58			
59						60					61			

21 Woods, in France
24 Egg producers
25 Not intoxicated
27 Colony member
28 Without question
29 Ziegfeld Follies costume designer
30 Ersatz bed, to Brits
31 Mount from which Moses saw Canaan
32 "___ the Air", movie starring George Clooney: 2 wds.
33 Bed cover
36 Occupies, as a table: 2 wds.
37 Coup d'___
39 Trainee
40 Close
42 To a greater extent: 2 wds.
43 Boss, slangily: 2 wds.
45 Christopher of "Superman"
46 Actress Carter and others
47 Person who lives outside their native country, for short
48 Kingdom on old Asian maps
49 Religious inscription, initially
50 Scottish capital, briefly
51 Small songbird
54 Suffix with fib or fist
55 Son of Noah

3

ACROSS

1 Spider's sense organ
5 "Fantastic!"
10 Assayed material
14 Wood sorrels
15 Growth regulating plant hormone
16 "Blue" or "White" river
17 Sap of life or energy
19 Brookings, e.g.: abbr.
20 Bitter feeling
21 Goes quickly
22 Target on a pool table
24 Leave hurriedly and secretly
26 Like some air fresheners
27 Fraction of a joule
28 Animal fat
29 High-tech recording medium, initially
32 Class of spirits in Muslim folklore
35 Snowbird
36 Labor group, initially
37 Clue
38 "Divine Comedy" poet
39 Leg's midpoint
40 Christie's "The ___ Murders"
41 Picture puzzle
42 Provided protective ditches
43 Money in Romania
44 Slept like ___: 2 wds.
45 Remote control abbr.
46 Man of many synonyms
48 Carpenter's coat
52 More lean
54 Difficult burden
55 Genetic material, initially
56 Jessica of the "Fantastic Four" films
57 Enlightening or astonishing disclosure
60 Lose hair
61 At attention
62 Cherry, e.g.
63 Foil alternative
64 They're often washed separately from whites
65 Band equipment, briefly

DOWN

1 Declamation stations
2 Biting
3 Uses soap and water
4 Letter after chi
5 Bleating like a sheep
6 Made a decision, as a judge
7 On what the Earth turns
8 Namely: abbr.
9 Alternative to a bikini: hyph.
10 Chilled: 2 wds.
11 Out of fashion: hyph.
12 Besides that
13 Stone paving block
18 Rose's danger

23 Cognizant of
25 Small price to pay
26 Small boats
28 Early time
30 On the safe side, at sea
31 Struck with the outer end of the head of a golf club
32 Indian dish made with stewed legumes: var.
33 Agree
34 Unable to be remedied
35 Lace cravat
38 Discouraged
39 Baking locale
41 Frenzy
42 Backs
45 Some strongrooms
47 Allocute
48 Sweater style: hyph.
49 Figure of speech
50 Nosy Parker
51 Arms' ends
52 Duplicate
53 Raindrop sound
54 In the past
58 Geologic time period
59 Bygone carrier's inits.

ACROSS

1 Mil. rank achieved by Buzz Aldrin
4 ___-bodied
8 Affirm
12 ___ list: hyph.
13 Adjective for Death Valley
14 Obscure
16 Lead
18 Liquid used to stimulate evacuation
19 Bakery attraction
20 Any minute
22 Cameo stone
23 Didn't walk
24 Flaky mineral
26 "A Nightmare on ___ Street"
28 Deep
29 Dolly, for one
30 Every last bit
33 Removable locks
36 "I'm ___ you!"
37 "___ on Goodness" ("Camelot" number)
38 Cordial
39 Beanie Babies, e.g.
40 Ancestry record
41 Of a thing
42 Pest
44 Abhorrent
46 Govt. property org.
47 ___ de Triomphe
48 Clarified butter in Indian cookery
49 Paid performer
50 Formerly, formerly
51 "Lord of the Rings" bad guy
54 ABM part
57 Canceled: 2 wds.
59 Piece with a purpose
61 Towns, informally
63 Disease causing stiffness of the joints
65 Cartoon genre with wide-eyed characters
66 Greek salad cheese
67 Crux
68 ___ bean
69 Put a halt to
70 Dundee denial

DOWN

1 Dried coconut meat
2 Ancient Greek theater
3 Gardener's bagful
4 "How very nice!"
5 Security error
6 Jungle climber
7 Tuber of taro
8 "How to Succeed in Business Without Really Trying" librettist Burrows
9 Snake poison
10 Where Adam and Eve were
11 Frosted
12 "A Life for the ___"
15 ___ out (stretch your credit card limit)
17 Flax-like fiber
21 2012 presidential candidate Gingrich

25 Diamonds, to hoods
27 "Titanic" actor DiCaprio
28 Engine speed, for short
29 Cut off
30 ___-American
31 In ___ of
32 Bottom of the barrel
33 Offshoot
34 Feed bag contents
35 "Superman II" villainess
36 Symbol of might
39 Airwaves regulator letters
40 1-1 game, say
42 Besmirch
43 Appliance on a board
44 Circus cries
45 Chill
48 Blue ___, sea cave of Capri
49 Miniature: var.
50 Cousin of a bittern
51 Old port on the Tiber
52 Bring up
53 Dermatologist's concern
54 "The ___ Daba Honeymoon"
55 Convent inhabitants
56 Threesome
58 Dunderheads
60 Put your name to
62 Caspian or North
64 W.W. II general ___ Arnold

5

ACROSS

1 ___ the cows come home
4 Dashboard inits.
7 Timber trees
12 Big brass instrument
13 Bauxite, e.g.
14 Gangsters ___ and Clyde
15 Sign that all are welcome: 2 wds.
17 City in Orange County, California
18 Celebration of a 300th anniversary
20 Visitor from outer space
21 Greek Hs
22 "Raiders of the Lost ___"
25 At sea
26 Egyptian fertility goddess
27 Eastern wrap: var.
29 Cord left hanging out as a sign of welcome
31 Billiards bounce
34 Be a cut above
35 Apparatus that transmits signals used for navigation: 2 wds.
39 Not fitting
40 Crazed
41 Dour
45 Beauty
46 Ado
47 Grimalkin
48 Essentials: 3 wds.
51 Carve
54 South American capital city
55 Bluish-purple
56 "Thanks a ___!"
57 Affirmations to pitchers
58 Receded
59 Farm animal
60 007, for one

DOWN

1 Mississippi city where Elvis was born
2 Genus that comprises the candytufts
3 Surgeon's tool
4 Earth's satellite
5 Raise an objection
6 Excommunication candidate
7 Fraction of an atmosphere
8 Deadly sin
9 It goes before E except after C: 2 wds.
10 All in the family
11 "Comprende?"
12 Add up
14 Bent
16 Cozy room
19 "Candy is dandy" writer
22 Bone-dry
23 Ashcroft's predecessor

■	1	2	3	■	4	5	6	■	■	7	8	9	10	11
12				■	13			■	14					
15				16				■	17					
18								19				■	■	■
20					■	21				■	■	22	23	24
25				■	26				■	27	28			
■	■	■	■	29					30					
■	31	32	33			■	■	■	34					■
35						36	37	38			■	■	■	■
39					■	40				■	41	42	43	44
45			■	■	46				■	47				
■	■	■	48	49					50					
51	52	53				■	54							
55						■	56			■	57			
58					■	■	59			■	60			■

24 Big holder of beer
26 "King Lear"'s foot
27 Bowl over
28 Gallery display
29 Cabbage
30 Chesapeake Bay term for the female of the blue crab
31 Bat Masterson weapon
32 First man on the scene
33 Stretch of turbulent water
35 Carpet
36 Has a little something
37 Friendly
38 Afro-Caribbean hairstyle
41 Parts of inner thighs
42 Walk with a bounce
43 Messy
44 Background items in Road Runner cartoons
46 "Leave it," to a typesetter
47 "How I Met Your Mother" network
48 Sight in Memphis
49 "Previously owned," in ad-speak
50 Anniversary, e.g.
51 "___ Got the World on a String"
52 Pen tip
53 Kernel's home

6

ACROSS

1 Congo, formerly
6 Beheaded Boleyn
10 Fan
14 Back-of-the-textbook section
15 Hang ominously
16 Language of Lahore
17 Where to play a round: 2 wds.
19 Bridle part
20 Opinion
21 "Let me see…"
22 Anon: 2 wds.
24 Annoyance
25 Bottom
26 Look-alike: 2 wds.
31 Actions
32 Conclusion
33 E-mail address ending for a general
35 In agreement: 2 wds.
36 ___-Atlantic
37 Goddess of the hunt
39 Like some scientists
40 ___ canto
41 Thick soup for picnics
42 Aggressive promotion of one's views, etc.: hyph.
46 Sounds of amazement
47 Honoree's spot
48 Flat upland area
51 Country north of Mex.
52 Attorneys' org.
55 Beat badly
56 Containers for fuzees
59 Beast
60 Chills and fever
61 Air freshener option
62 ___ Sea (highly saline body of water)
63 Places for props
64 Fragrant resin

DOWN

1 Makes a sharp turn
2 Dwarf buffalo
3 One way to stand by
4 Basketball game figure with a whistle, for short
5 Swop
6 College graduates
7 "___ any drop to drink": Coleridge
8 Part of a horse's bridle
9 Beryl variety
10 Large migratory shorebird
11 ___ balls (chocolate covered treats)
12 Father of Balder
13 Respiratory organ
18 Drops
23 "Humanum ___ errare"

24 Sean of "Mystic River"
26 Greek letters
27 LED part
28 Puts a roof on
29 Adult insect
30 Curtain fabric
31 Beaver's structure
34 "7 Faces of Dr. ___"
36 House and lands, legally
37 Subject to import tax
38 "Under the Net" author Murdoch
40 Island country, capital Nassau
41 Full of chutzpah
43 Divided into groups for auction
44 Adversary
45 Brings out
48 Egg on
49 Theater section
50 Enveloping glow
52 Car bar
53 Board the Enterprise, with "aboard"
54 Fungal spore sacs
57 "For shame!"
58 Alberta resource

ACROSS

1 Champagne stopper
5 "It's no ___!"
8 Reconnoiters
14 Beneficial bestowal
15 Score on the diamond
16 It's attractive on the fridge
17 Fairground booth used for firing rifles: 2 wds.
20 D.C. org.
21 Business abbr.
22 Duke's counterpart
23 Ballad ending
25 A pitcher likes a low one
27 "Be quiet!"
29 ___'wester
30 Passage
32 Herd members
34 Pleasant
35 High degree, initially
37 Part of the gene pool, initially
38 Crosses with loops
40 Physics unit
42 Bamboozled
46 Light knock
48 "Indeedy"
50 Winged goddess of victory
51 Relating to marriage, legally
55 One that got away
57 Chance
58 Health resort
59 2016 Olympics city, for short
60 Clairvoyant's ability, initially
61 Cher's voice range
63 Augur
65 City in Tex.
67 Where to board a train: 2 wds.
72 Bible book after Proverbs: abbr.
73 "Holy moly!"
74 On a single occasion
75 "___ Street" (famous kids' show)
76 Artist's asset
77 Medieval alcoholic drink

DOWN

1 "JAG" network
2 "___ Baby Baby" (Linda Ronstadt hit)
3 Framework fitted on top of a car: 2 wds.
4 Door feature
5 Altdorf's canton
6 Catch the rays
7 M.I.T. grad: abbr.
8 Atom ___ (physicist's equipment)
9 "Silent" president, familiarly
10 Eye
11 Anxiety
12 Brat
13 Record player needle
18 Associations
19 "Wow!"

23 It's active in Sicily
24 "___ Go Bragh!" (Irish)
26 Upholstery problem
28 Female deer
31 India's first P.M.
33 Animals
36 Drought-stricken
39 Backtalk
41 Channel Island to the north-west of Jersey
43 Gas conveyor
44 ___ out (manages)
45 "___ Space Nine"
47 Native American infant
49 Pressure unit: abbr.
51 Uses jointly
52 Royal residence
53 Field of vision?
54 Dalai ___
56 Closing passage
62 Earthen container
64 Little advantage
66 Little bit of matter
68 Band that broke up in 2011
69 Athletic supporter?
70 Wood sorrel
71 1970 Jagger film "___ Kelly"

8

ACROSS

1 Flemish painter Jan van ___
5 Sony product, e.g.: abbr., 2 wds.
9 Swing voters: abbr.
13 Dappled sorrel, chestnut, or bay
14 Indy driver Luyendyk
15 Actor Frobe of "Goldfinger"
16 Tyra Banks, e.g.
19 Manhattan Project scientist
20 Edge along some mountaintops
21 Stuck: 3 wds.
23 Baseball great Rose
24 Gravitate (toward)
25 Smith and Jones, maybe
28 "Agreed": 3 wds.
32 Cooking fats
33 Banda ___ (Sumatran city)
34 Quadrennial games org.
35 Has a mortgage
36 Bid
38 Soldier of fortune, briefly
39 Biddy
40 Chinese gelatin
41 Mediterranean island, capital Valletta
42 In a proficient manner
44 Belonging to some prior time
46 "Dies ___" (hymn)
47 "Dinner at the Homesick Restaurant" novelist Tyler
48 Bony
51 Case
55 Playwright Connelly
56 Constantly: 3 wds.
58 "A Letter for ___" (1945 film)
59 Actor Morales
60 Webzine
61 Beaks
62 Coarse file
63 News feeds for Web users, initially

DOWN

1 Formerly, once
2 Part of BYOB
3 ___ of Good Hope
4 Volleyball players' equipment
5 Descendant of Noah's son
6 Worker bees
7 Environmental conservation concern
8 Certain intersection
9 Crested pet
10 Soft ball material
11 Eins, zwei, ___
12 River to the underworld
17 Like Boston accents, as it were: hyph.
18 German songs
22 "The Turtle" poet

24 Adult nits
25 Hello, in Hawaii
26 Litigated, old-style
27 "Goodnight" girl of song
29 Highway sign
30 A bit, colloquially
31 Philosopher William of ___
33 It's south of Eur.
36 Member of the Siouan people
37 Dunaway who played Bonnie
38 Femme fatale: hyph.
40 Razor brand name
41 ___ Carlo
43 Parts of a whole
44 Company with a kangaroo logo
45 Remove from the vessel
48 Augur's concern
49 Put away
50 Chicago daily, for short
51 Rick's love in "Casablanca"
52 Steals, old-style
53 Certain Nashville trophies, for short
54 Brain activity records, initially
57 Celtic sea god

9

ACROSS

1 "The World of Suzie ___" (1960 movie)
5 With, in Paris
9 Like Beethoven
13 Yucatan years
14 Burkina ___
15 Abbr. at the bottom of a business letter
16 11 November occasion: 2 wds.
19 Rikki-tikki-___
20 Rabat's nation
22 Amusement place: 2 wds.
26 Different or potent ending
27 Poker declaration: 2 wds.
28 Pooh's creator
29 "Que ___?"
30 Federal agcy., 1946–75
31 "___ Ha'i"
32 Needing practice
33 Potpourri piece, perhaps: 2 wds.
36 Muscle weakness
39 African flower
40 Rate at which computer data is transferred, initially
43 Basalt source
44 Pope John Paul II's real first name
46 Misfortunes
47 ___ out a win
48 Like the street grid of Midtown Manhattan
50 React to yeast
52 "___ Yankees"
53 Front runner: hyph., 2 wds.
58 Combine
59 "___ you don't!": 2 wds.
60 Auto clb.
61 Karate weapons
62 W.W. II server
63 By way of, briefly

DOWN

1 More than a battle
2 Former: hyph.
3 Wandering
4 Bygone multinational political group (1976–1997): 2 wds.
5 Place for mil. planes
6 Alt. spelling
7 Hockey's Tikkanen
8 Swindler: 2 wds.
9 Caterpillar competitor
10 Inner prefix
11 Small trees
12 Angle: hyph.
17 "O Sole ___"
18 It follows zip or bar
21 Body wash brand
22 ___ Veneto

23 Latin 101 verb

24 Agitate

25 Ready-made computer images: 2 wds.

29 Afghan coin

31 Lad

32 Canada's Arctic explorer

33 Biology class, initially

34 Morlock morsels in "The Time Machine"

35 Cost to cross

36 Hebrew leader

37 Remove (clothes): 2 wds.

38 Outstanding

40 Flaw

41 Relating to the sole of the foot

42 Belarus, once, initially

44 Game with a caller

45 TV ad phrase: 2 wds.

46 Bogged down: 3 wds.

48 Bowling alley button

49 Ceremony words: 2 wds.

51 Gds.: abbr.

54 Loan overseer, initially

55 Comedic actress Gasteyer

56 Grammatical case: abbr.

57 Bygone money

10

ACROSS

1 "Am I invisible over here?"
5 Teri of "After Hours"
9 "...your cake and ___, too": 2 wds.
14 Vega's constellation
15 Initially, they travel very long distances
16 Copy an outline
17 Trompe l'___ (optical illusion)
18 Space-based observatory launched in 1983
19 Label for Arab meat dealers
20 Harriet Beecher Stowe novel: 3 wds.
23 Cub Scout leaders, in the UK
24 Roll-___ (some deodorant sticks)
25 An empty bottle is full of it
26 Some RBI producers: abbr.
28 Elko-to-Reno dir.
31 Hoity-toity sorts
34 "See ya," in Siena
35 Stage direction for an actress ("alone"): 2 wds.
36 Bob Hope film of 1951: 4 wds.
39 "Das Lied von der ___"
40 Angler's need: 2 wds.
41 Considers
42 Carrier to Oslo, shortly
43 Cell messenger letters
44 Cholesterol carrier, initially
45 Band booking
46 Hoi ___
49 "Why ask me?": 4 wds.
54 Costa del Sol attraction
55 India.___, singer of "Little Things"
56 Exploding star
57 Expertise
58 Dressmaker's needs
59 College srs. may sit for them
60 Gurus
61 At ___ time (prearranged): 2 wds.
62 Pol. divisions prior to 1991

DOWN

1 1994 NL Manager of the Year
2 Animal known for its laugh
3 World Poker Tour champion Lindgren
4 Pliant
5 Instrument for Segovia
6 Big dos
7 Go here and there
8 Blog feeds, initially
9 Patriot Allen and author Canin
10 Most Meccans
11 Anklebones
12 Optimistic credo: 2 wds.
13 ___ Aviv
21 "Beloved" actress Kimberly
22 Green or blue, e.g.

26 Memorable Martin et al.
27 1990s pop group Color Me ___
28 Left the land of Nod
29 Slender
30 Bankrolls
31 Holy Fr. women
32 Drag racing org.
33 Big ref. works, for short
34 Mrs. Dithers in "Blondie"
35 Transliterators' troubles
37 Skin disease of mammals
38 In a peculiar manner
43 Opponents
44 Sure to tell the truth
45 Country crooner Crystal
46 "Rights of Man" author
47 Air freshener targets
48 "What did ___ do to you?": 2 wds.
49 Actress Chase
50 Former Defense Secretary Alexander
51 Auto parts giant, initially
52 Speaker of baseball
53 "The law is ___..." (Dickens): 2 wds.
54 Ltr. addenda

11

ACROSS

1 Clutch
6 Acquire
10 Hawaii's other Mauna
13 Part of a TV feed
14 M-1, for one
15 Under the weather
16 Placed high in a series of preferred candidates
18 18-wheeler
19 "48 ___" (Eddie Murphy movie)
20 Publicizes in an exaggerated way
21 Hindu loincloth
23 Cyclotron particle
24 "Ocean's ___"
25 Expendable soldiers: 2 wds.
31 One way to be taken
32 Being broadcast, as a radio show: 2 wds.
33 ___ Beta Kappa
36 Drab
37 ___ of law
38 Den denizen
39 Capitol Hill V.I.P.: abbr.
40 Life of luxury and pleasure, la ___ vita
41 Ship board
42 Hold the ___, have control of expenditure: 2 wds.
44 Drink
47 "Sure", slangily
48 Dog breed
49 Flies high
52 Go downhill for fun
55 Father's Day gift
56 Gaping with surprise or astonishment: hyph.
59 Ashes holder
60 Reduce stock to nothing: 2 wds.
61 Augusta is its capital
62 Put in rollers, as hair
63 Drinks a bit
64 Montreal team

DOWN

1 Cut
2 Duisburg's locale
3 Bothers
4 "Can I help you, ___?"
5 S-shaped object used for suspending a kettle over a fire: hyph.
6 Acclivity
7 Baby newts
8 Black and tan beverage
9 Traveling salesman
10 Bolshoi rival, once
11 "Who's Who" group
12 Gum used especially as a thickener
14 Cheat, slangily
17 City between Boston and Salem
22 That woman's
23 Mark of a ruler
24 Alter a "Life" sentence?
25 Airport vehicles

1	2	3	4	5			6	7	8	9		10	11	12
13						14						15		
16					17							18		
19				20						21	22			
			23						24					
25	26	27				28	29	30						
31						32						33	34	35
36					37						38			
39				40						41				
			42						43					
44	45	46							47					
48						49	50	51				52	53	54
55				56	57						58			
59				60						61				
62				63						64				

26 Possessing the know-how
27 Indian bread
28 Chumps
29 Chilling: 2 wds.
30 Copenhageners
33 Hymn of praise: var.
34 Put on the wall
35 Bothers
37 Dermatologist's concern
38 Radar screen dot
40 Open to doubt or suspicion
41 Take to be the case
42 "Babe: ___ in the City" (1998 sequel)
43 Pro's opposite
44 Fit or seizure
45 Wavelike design
46 Sportscaster Musburger
49 Percolate
50 ___ probandi
51 Rock blaster: abbr.
52 Camel, metaphorically
53 Game of chance
54 "Beware the ___ of March", soothsayer's advice to Julius Caesar
57 ___ particle
58 Bill addition

12

ACROSS

1 Hello, in Honolulu
6 "Hurlyburly" Tony winner Judith
10 Acad. values
14 Apres-ski drink
15 "True Colors" actress Merrill
16 Professional sportswriter and boxing expert Kevin
17 Buck passer?: 2 wds.
20 Expired
21 "Trial of the Century" figure Kaelin
22 Decree
23 Gelatinize
24 Communicate silently
25 Bric-a-___
26 A.F.L.'s partner
27 Island in the Taiwan Strait
29 Australian bird
32 Disdain
35 Single-named supermodel
36 Mark Harmon series on CBS
37 Island in Massachusetts: 2 wds.
40 Gremlins
41 Great Lakes State separate education program, initially
42 Picasso's hat
43 Island where Brando lived: abbr.
44 Big East team: abbr.
45 Delivery room doctors, for short
46 Wings: Lat.
48 Chows down
50 Flit (about)
53 Kind of column
55 Guesstimate words: 2 wds.
56 Musical sound
57 Song recorded by Jackie Wilson in 1963: 3 wds.
60 Seating area
61 Years abroad
62 Easy out in baseball: hyph.
63 Small storage building
64 Deck crew's boss, briefly
65 "___ of pottage" (what Esau sold his birthright for): 2 wds.

DOWN

1 Certain learning places, briefly
2 Danny DeVito's role in "Taxi"
3 Group of eight
4 Coat part
5 U.S.A.F. weapon
6 Luggage attachment: 2 wds.
7 Washington memorial dedicatees: 2 wds.
8 Prefix meaning "within"
9 China's Sun ___-sen
10 Comedian Radner
11 Cop's auto: 2 wds.
12 "Smart" guy
13 Muralist José Maria ___
18 Sony co-founder Morita
19 Mysterious: var.
24 Hyperbolic sine

1	2	3	4	5	■	6	7	8	9	■	10	11	12	13
14					■	15				■	16			
17					18					19				
20				■	21				■	22				
23			■	24				■	25				■	■
■	■	■	26			■	27	28			■	29	30	31
32	33	34			■	35				■	36			
37					38					39				
40				■	41				■	42				
43			■	44				■	45			■	■	■
■	■	46	47			■	48	49			■	50	51	52
53	54				■	55				■	56			
57					58					59				
60				■	61				■	62				
63				■	64				■	65				

25 Beethoven's birthplace
26 Components of some PCs
28 Time for Funchal flores
30 Bog
31 DOT, alternatively
32 Slugged, old-style
33 Bed, in Spanish
34 Home for kids without parents
35 "The City ___ War" (Cobra Starship song): 2 wds.
36 Humorist Bill and comedian Louis
38 French friend
39 Declines
44 Horse's motion
45 Midwest Indian
47 Enjoyed
49 Welcome guests: 2 wds.
50 Flip out: 2 wds.
51 Elephant goad
52 Oceanic abysses
53 There are many in the Pacific Ocean: abbr.
54 Eager cry: hyph.
55 "Curses!": 2 wds.
56 ___ McAn shoes
58 Rest time: abbr.
59 Marienbad, for one

13

ACROSS

1 Brazilian novelist Jorge
6 Floor it
11 City, in slang
14 Drainage spot
15 Concealed
16 Cambodia's Lon ___
17 Proof of completion
19 ___ Aquarids (May meteor shower)
20 Suffix with superficial or stupid
21 Departs
22 Certain television recorders
24 Animal shelter
25 Yellow
27 Bring to light
30 Deep dish
31 Pope of 1605: 2 wds.
32 Very quick
33 "Kapow!"
36 Suffix with utter or annoy
37 Carefree runs
38 Adult female horse
39 Northeast Caucasian language
40 Actor Affleck
41 Cajun veggies
42 Brought forth
44 Decides one will: 2 wds.
45 Give a date: 2 wds.
47 "Break ___!" (to an actor): 2 wds.
48 End, as a subscription
49 "Our Time in ___" (10,000 Maniacs album)
50 Certain detectives, initially
53 Shiba ___ (dog breed)
54 Cause trouble, slangily: 3 wds.
58 Atlanta-based public health agcy.
59 Founded: abbr.
60 Zoe Saldana role
61 Cry in cartoons
62 Has beens, probably: hyph.
63 Place

DOWN

1 Fungal spore sacs
2 Encounter
3 Not as intended
4 Largest city in Mich.
5 Japanese art of folding paper
6 Peeping Tom
7 Chest muscles, briefly
8 Detergent brand
9 Erie hrs.
10 Performed with another
11 Gymnastics event: 2 wds.
12 Magazine sections
13 Late Bill of fashion
18 Pâté de ___ gras
23 ___ de la cité
24 De ___ (expensive)
25 Aquarium fish
26 "A God in Ruins" novelist

27 Airline to Israel: 2 wds.
28 "Hercules" spinoff
29 Get it in the goal!: 2 wds.
30 Domesticated
32 1953 A.L. M.V.P.
34 Like ___ in a trap: 2 wds.
35 Middle: prefix
37 Autumn tool
38 Dept. that works with Sales
40 Became united
41 Becomes less emotionally guarded: 2 wds.
43 Autos nicknamed "Bugs", initially
44 Olive genus
45 Clear soda brand
46 "Gene Simmons Family Jewels" channel: 3 wds.
47 "Must we not pay ___ to pleasure, too?": Wilmot: 2 wds.
49 Those things in Tijuana
50 1920s–50s papal name
51 Crucifix letters
52 Three-handed card game
55 Communication for the deaf, initially
56 "Lord, is ___?" (Last Supper question)
57 Despite, in poems

14

ACROSS

1 Black bird
4 Court helper: hyph.
8 Had in one's hands
12 Former Vikings coach Mike
13 Half of Mork's sign-off, on "Mork & Mindy"
14 French romance
16 Inkling
17 Forest ox
18 Feelings
19 Costly, as a victory
21 Mets and Marlins div.
23 2002 British Open champion
24 Ban
25 AFC South team on scoreboards
27 News initials
29 Rap group based in Southern Chicago
31 "Reader" on the newsstands
35 Worked up
39 Big put-on
40 Great Society pres.
41 Medical application
43 "Little" car of song, initially
44 Country that borders Vietnam and Thailand
46 Words of praise: 3 wds.
49 "___ quam videri" (North Carolina's motto)
50 AAA offering
51 Class-conscious org.?
52 U.S.A.F. decoration
54 Anxiety and trauma, for some
58 Light units: abbr.
61 Dental org.
63 Garage floor blemish: 2 wds.
65 Former Texas senator Phil
67 "Life" founder Henry
69 Balsam used in perfumery
70 "A Delicate Balance" playwright
71 Adherents: suffix
72 Fall site in Genesis
73 Arrange in a tournament
74 Rotten little kid
75 ___ Speedwagon (music group)

DOWN

1 "___ ever wonder…": 2 wds.
2 Sour-tasting
3 Fatigue: 2 wds.
4 ___ B'rith (Jewish organization)
5 French bench
6 Palindromic artist
7 10 jiao
8 Any port in a storm
9 Former big record label initials
10 Brain section
11 Face-off
12 Put a point on, old-style
15 System for distributing news to Web users, initially
20 Arizona Indian
22 Golf ball position
26 Head slapper's cry

28 Aegean island on which Homer is said to be buried
29 Round dance
30 Divided avenue: abbr.
32 West African country
33 28-state gp.
34 Bk. after Gen.
35 Letter before eme in the Spanish alphabet
36 Budding entrepreneurs, for short
37 Spanish eyes
38 Serpent deity group, in Hinduism
42 German numeral
45 But, to a Roman
47 ___ of approval
48 Comedian
50 Buddhist Beastie Boy, initially
53 Of renown
55 Lyric poem
56 Floating log competition
57 Flabbergast
58 N.Y.C. airport
59 WWW addresses
60 "Quién ___?"
62 "Boola Boola" singers
63 Prefix denoting "eight"
64 Superlative suffix
66 Chinese dish made with noodles
68 "Anchors Aweigh" gp.

15

ACROSS

1 Ab strengthener: hyph.
6 Mischief maker
9 One of Snow White's buddies
12 "Consider Yourself" musical
14 Nothing at all
15 Copycat
17 Total: 2 wds.
18 Perpetually cold level on a mountain
20 Compass point: hyph.
22 Cutter with a broad blade
24 ___ noir
25 Amusing water creature
26 Bar
29 Captain, e.g.
31 He saves the day
32 Woman's control undergarment: 2 wds.
35 Gumdrop flavor
36 Common observation
40 Patriot
45 Edible fish
49 Traveled
50 Ladies of the house, informally
51 Gets bested
53 Big sip
55 Drinking vessel
56 Not impressive
60 More determined or brave
61 Comfort in distress
64 Accessory for Miss America
65 "First Blood" director Kotcheff
66 Fine-grained mineral with a soft feel
67 Bad-mouth, slangily
68 Double curve
69 Long bag nets used to catch fish

DOWN

1 Coll. course
2 U.N. agcy. concerned with working conditions
3 One of 24 longitudinal divisions of the globe: 2 wds.
4 Iris holder
5 Animals at home
6 To such an extent
7 Number from which another is to be subtracted
8 Connive
9 Fourth Hebrew letter: var.
10 Sleep inducer
11 Ceremonial burner
13 Campus military org.
16 Nostalgia-evoking
19 "___ am I kidding?"
21 Delhi dress
22 "Antony and Cleopatra" prop
23 Indian dish made with stewed legumes: var.

27 Bank amenity letters

28 Center of French resistance in W.W. II

30 Hate group

33 Bite like a beaver

34 Cheese in a ball

37 ___ king: 2 wds.

38 Cheap and showy ornament

39 Abraham's grandson

41 Those who take exams

42 Toward the center

43 Auditory

44 80 minims: abbr.

45 Punches

46 Joseph ___, author of "The Arrow of Gold"

47 Birthplace of St. Francis

48 Most remote parts of the sea

52 "Quiet on the ___!"

54 Big blow

57 Commend

58 Do nothing

59 Comrade in arms

62 Act as a prompter

63 Germany's Dortmund-___ Canal

16

ACROSS

1 Frat party need
4 Dashboard gauge, briefly
8 Humiliate, old-style
14 Binary digit
15 Turkish honorific
16 Meaningful talk
17 PIN requester
18 Face-off
19 Fine wool
20 General principle of non-interference: hyph.
23 Hokkaido people
24 Rushes past
28 Goo
30 More, in Managua
32 Prenatal test, for short
33 Totaled
36 ___ Aviv (city in Israel)
37 Certain political pundit
42 Dadaism founder
43 Sides
44 Unmoving
47 "___ be a shame if …"
48 Lightened (up)
52 Part of F.B.I.
54 It may precede old age
55 Believing in more than one god
60 Put to the test: 2 wds.
63 Phone, slangily
64 Compact submachine gun
65 Tibetan guide
66 Crazily
67 Detachable container
68 Bill
69 Like a busybody
70 Ed.'s request

DOWN

1 Cuddly animals from Australia
2 Call for
3 Star sign
4 Small fry
5 Malaria symptom
6 At the home of
7 0.5
8 Let in
9 ___ Nevada (mountain range)
10 Women's quarters in a Muslim house: var.
11 2001 Will Smith movie
12 Calendar abbr.
13 Inflated sense of self-worth
21 Shrub that causes dermatitis
22 Gave one's word
25 Against

1	2	3		4	5	6	7		8	9	10	11	12	13
14				15					16					
17				18					19					
20			21					22						
23								24				25	26	27
28				29		30	31			32				
			33		34				35			36		
37	38	39								40	41			
42					43									
44			45	46		47				48		49	50	51
52					53						54			
			55				56	57	58	59				
60	61	62					63					64		
65							66					67		
68							69					70		

26 Capital of Ukraine

27 It's under a foot

29 Old name for Tokyo

30 In a sloppy way

31 Crack

34 "CSI" topic, often

35 Pipe material, for short

37 Artless one

38 Fish-eating eagle

39 Kind of column: hyph.

40 Ended a fast

41 Autocrats of old

45 News write-up

46 Group of actors

49 Stomach-flattening exercises: hyph.

50 Animal parasites

51 Make a choice

53 Place to exchange rings

56 Compared to

57 The human genus

58 Archer with wings

59 Deep black

60 Amt. of sugar

61 Density symbol

62 "Absolutely!"

17

ACROSS

1 Vitalities, vigors
5 Left slightly open
9 Part in "The Devil's Disciple" played by Cheryl Maiker
14 Melville tale of the South Pacific
15 Common small crake
16 Indian honorific
17 2010 Apple blockbuster
18 Attention ___
19 Backup procedure: 2 wds.
20 Arrangement of stars
23 Ending for Sudan or Taiwan
24 "Is ___?": 2 wds.
25 Riddle-me-___ (rhyme)
26 ABC morning show, for short
29 Subway handhold
31 Water nymph
33 Chop down
34 Fed. property overseer
36 Online feed, initially
37 Battery for small devices, initially
38 It entails living happily ever after: 2 wds.
43 "Reader's Digest" co-founder Wallace
44 Erstwhile radio duo, ___ and Abner
45 King, in Portugal
46 Makers of Athlon, Duron and Sempron processors, initially
47 Coup ___
49 Twisted
53 "Uh-huh"
54 Halifax clock setting: inits.
55 Camel-hair coat
57 Keanu Reeves's character in "The Matrix"
58 Actor who played Steve Jobs in "Jobs": 2 wds.
62 Actionable words
64 Crystal ball user
65 Fashion designer Gernreich
66 Friends, in Firenze
67 Ending for cigar
68 "To Live and Die ___" (1985 film): 2 wds
69 Spike Lee's "She's ___ Have It"
70 "Unto us ___ is given": 2 wds.
71 "After that ..."

DOWN

1 Gives an opinion
2 Duty on foreign goods
3 Complainer
4 Installs, as an outfield
5 Liability's opposite
6 "Maple Leaf Rag" composer Scott
7 Asia's shrinking ___ Sea
8 Took a chance: 3 wds.
9 Spotted
10 American historian of Jewish ancestry, Professor ___ Baron
11 Chinese port on the estuary of the Yangtze
12 "Am ___ trouble?": 2 wds.
13 Fall back, as the tide

1	2	3	4	■	5	6	7	8	■	9	10	11	12	13
14				■	15				■	16				
17				■	18				■	19				
20				21					22				■	■
23			■	24			■	25			■	26	27	28
29			30		■	31	32				■	33		
■	■	■	34		35	■	36			■	37			
38	39	40				41				42				
43				■	44			■	45			■	■	■
46			■	47				48	■	49		50	51	52
53			■	54			■	55	56		■	57		
■	■	58	59				60				61			
62	63				■	64				■	65			
66					■	67				■	68			
69					■	70				■	71			

21 Blotto
22 Device for combing wool
27 Statistician's middle
28 Like gossiping tongues
30 Taj Mahal locale
32 Pleasant inhalation
35 Most competent
37 "Grazie ___!" (Italian for "Thank God!"): 2 wds.
38 Bump off
39 Noon or midnight
40 It's hard to break: 2 wds.
41 Lemmon/Matthau cruise movie: 3 wds.
42 Not yet used to: 2 wds.
47 Showy bloom
48 Become fond of: 2 wds.
50 "Nosirreebob"
51 Sewing item
52 "The Picture of ___ Gray", Oscar Wilde novel
56 President Martin Van ___
59 Branch
60 Brings home
61 Art class feedback session, slangily
62 Fall back
63 "As I see it," online

18

ACROSS

1 Kid-lit Dr. ___
6 Light bulb's home
10 Light and insubstantial
14 In ___ (agitated): 2 wds.
15 Berry in some energy boosters
16 Dog's irritation
17 Whiskey and candy drink: 3 wds.
19 Use ___ lose …: 2 wds.
20 Christine, Eileen in "Hateship, Loveship"
21 Officially noted: 2 wds.
23 German exclamation
25 News
26 Dollar, slangily
31 ___-Cat (winter vehicle)
32 Martinique et Guadeloupe, e.g.
33 Madrid Mrs.
34 "For want of ___, the shoe was lost": 2 wds.
38 Bric-a-___
39 Shocked with a device
42 Nos. on checks
43 ___ example: 2 wds.
45 Nonprofessional sports grp.
46 Amount owing
47 Trains: abbr.
49 Oafs
51 Dutch oven
55 Govt. agency founded in 1953, initially
56 Cutter of gemstones
58 More peculiar
62 Eye, in Paris
63 Makers of the Trent and Merlin aircraft engines: hyph.
66 Letters of introduction?
67 Duel tool
68 Absolutely perfect
69 Narrow margin of victory
70 Jacques who directed "The Umbrellas of Cherbourg"
71 Animals' backs

DOWN

1 Mediterranean isl.
2 Class for foreigners, for short
3 Donald Duck, to his nephews
4 Guru Nanak, e.g.
5 Relating to a nation
6 Young fellow
7 Prefix with bat or phobia
8 Old-fashioned contraction
9 Heatherlike shrub
10 Buff
11 "Candle in the Wind" composer John
12 Alteration of a corporation's structure: abbr.
13 Football measurements
18 Most pleasant
22 Author O'Brien

1	2	3	4	5		6	7	8	9		10	11	12	13
14						15					16			
17					18						19			
	20						21			22				
				23		24		25						
26	27	28	29				30		31					
32					33					34		35	36	37
38					39			40	41		42			
43				44			45				46			
			47		48		49			50				
51	52	53				54		55						
56							57		58		59	60	61	
62					63			64						65
66					67					68				
69					70					71				

24 Bar mitzvah dance

26 Bros, e.g.

27 The king, in Italian: 2 wds.

28 Butcher's stock

29 Irish dramatist and wit (1854–1900): 2 wds.

30 Kind of spray

35 Card that rivals MC

36 Beatles' song, "Let___": 2 wds.

37 D-Day carriers, initially

40 Waters: Fr.

41 Blockheads

44 "Blue" TV lawmen

48 Rose high in the air

50 Capital of Spain

51 "Wake of the Ferry" painter

52 Exercise technique based on martial arts: hyph.

53 Heroic narratives

54 Metaphor

57 Primordial matter of the universe

59 Extinct bird

60 Ogler

61 Some TVs' letters

64 Science writer Willy ___

65 Guidonian note

19

ACROSS

1 Atlas plates
5 Intrepid
11 Cold War monogram
14 Yelp of sudden pain
15 Winter fisherman's tool: 2 wds.
16 "Alley-___!"
17 Half-human, half-Betazoid "Star Trek" character Deanna
18 Biological groups
19 "Respect for Acting" author Hagen
20 Marine arthropod with a domed carapace: 2 wds.
23 ___ polloi (common people)
24 Eastern European
27 Mandela's org.
30 Name-droppers
34 #2 Bill Withers hit of 1972: 2 wds.
35 Boxing prize
37 Sting operation
38 Fools
39 Impending evil or danger: 3 wds.
42 Sewing cases
43 "I'm so hungry, I could ___ horse!": 2 wds.
44 Aesop animal who snoozes and loses
45 Signal agreement: 2 wds.
46 Cheri formerly of "SNL"
48 Designer monogram under the Gucci label
49 Longtime Magic 8 Ball maker
50 Efron of "High School Musical"
52 Rare person or thing: 4 wds.
61 104 in Roman numerals
63 Grab greedily: 2 wds.
64 Sidi ___, Morocco
65 "___ to a Nightingale"
66 Princess Leia ___
67 "You're So ___" (Carly Simon song)
68 Est., once
69 Immure: 2 wds.
70 Ending for kitchen or luncheon

DOWN

1 Fable
2 ___ Flite (bicycle brand)
3 Poverty-stricken
4 Brushing or rustling sound
5 Inquires: 2 wds.
6 Banda ___ (Indonesian city)
7 Attorney General Janet
8 Crystal ball gazer's phrase: 2 wds.
9 Bust maker
10 Heavy metal band known for its grotesque costumes
11 Baseball feat: 2 wds.
12 "i" lid
13 Antipollution grp.
21 Goddess of the dawn

22 Intrinsically: 2 wds.
25 Rulers in Africa or Arabia: var.
26 Craft
27 Missing, as from class
28 Child's wish for Christmas: 2 wds.
29 Extent to which the blue sky is hidden: 2 wds.
31 Monteverdi opera
32 Unable to do a thing well: 2 wds.
33 Rush
34 Japanese vegetable
36 Moon of Neptune
40 Brit. award
41 Almond confection
47 Potent or penitent ending
51 Novelist Barker
53 Those, in Spain
54 About: 2 wds.
55 Serpent deity group, in Hinduism
56 "Come on, be ___!": 2 wds.
57 1936 Pasteur portrayer Paul
58 "___ first you …": 2 wds.
59 Attending to the task at hand: 2 wds.
60 Muse count
61 Corporations: abbr.
62 Border-crossing necessities

20

ACROSS

1 Donkey, to Domingo
5 Doctor's prefix with -ologist
9 Old Commodore computer
14 Coast-to-coast highway: 2 wds.
15 Tab grabber's words: 2 wds.
16 Locks up
17 Hotel convenience
18 "Sayonara" Oscar winner: 2 wds.
20 Seed again
22 Fat substitute
23 Courtyards
24 City in Lyon County, Iowa
26 U.K. reference set
27 World-renowned clarinetist from New Orleans: 2 wds.
31 Former dictator ___ Amin
32 Actor Stephen of "V for Vendetta"
33 "Are we alone?" prog.
36 "___ to You", 1994 romcom starring Nicolas Cage and Bridget Fonda: 3 wds.
41 One-named singer for the 1960s Velvet Underground
42 "There's no ___ T-E-A-M": 2 wds.
43 "The Sultan of Sulu" writer
45 Bagel topper: 2 wds.
50 Only three-letter element
53 Fawn over, with "on"
54 "Julius Caesar" role
55 Orbital extremes
58 Gospel
59 Overly affectionate, colloquially: hyph.
62 Tara of "American Pie"
64 "Go on, ___ you!": 2 wds.
65 Four, in Germany
66 Fishing eagle
67 Thoreau work, "Faith in ___": 2 wds.
68 ___ account: never: 2 wds.
69 Exam for would-be attys.

DOWN

1 "___ for Alibi" (Sue Grafton mystery): 2 wds.
2 Began: 2 wds.
3 Ancient Egyptian queen
4 Baby's garment
5 Neighbor of Swed.
6 Chemical suffix
7 College Park school, home of the Terrapins, initially
8 Start one's PC up again
9 Molière play part
10 Gymnastics cushions
11 Patsy Cline's "___ Pieces": 3 wds.
12 Literary category
13 Longtime Syrian president
19 Arm bone
21 Clumsy fool
23 Bee: prefix

24 Face-off
25 Counting calories: 3 wds.
28 Sch. in Tulsa, Oklahoma
29 DSL offerer
30 India neighbor, briefly
34 Truckers
35 Peninsula of southeastern Asia
37 Medical amts.
38 "___-Pah-Pah", song from "Oliver!"
39 Tannery skin
40 Ques. counterpart
44 Bambi's aunt
46 Had too much, for short
47 Balkan area, capital Priština
48 Like a lot of clues in this puzzle: abbr.
49 Hardy partner
50 Sylvester's "Rocky" co-star
51 Some digital audio players
52 Astronomy wonders
56 "Pretty Woman" star Richard
57 "Brown ___ Girl" (Van Morrison hit)
58 Apprentice
60 Beaujolais, e.g.
61 Early night, in an ode
63 Michigan's biggest city: abbr.

21

ACROSS

1 Gutter locale
5 ___ problem with (doesn't like): 2 wds.
9 Get red
14 Former Russian ruler: var.
15 "If ___ a hammer...": 2 wds.
16 Bridge positions
17 Bobby Darin's label until 1963
18 Dismantles: 2 wds.
20 Little, in Lille
21 Dr.'s orders
22 Latin examples, briefly
23 Neighbor of Colombia
25 Gifts
29 Gender abbr.
30 Alpine stream
31 Tooth-doctors' org.
32 Hosp. aide
33 Ron on whom "Born on the Fourth of July" was based
35 Perform an electrician's job
36 "Beowulf" beverage
37 B'nai ___
38 Rank-smelling
39 Gospel singer Winans
40 Not too hot, like a burner: 2 wds.
41 1974 John Wayne cop movie
42 Off. worker
43 Ancient gathering place
44 Brother of Cain
46 "The Cup of Tea" painter Mary
48 Twists of fate
51 Neb. neighbor
52 Some community bldgs.
53 "Shh!", to Schoenberg
54 Work on canvas that combines paint, ink, and collage: 2 wds.
58 Humane org.
59 1950s candidate Stevenson
60 Actor and director Sean
61 ___ Phelps, aka SNL's "The Ladies' Man"
62 "Beau ___"
63 Perseverance motto starter: 2 wds.
64 Crumbs

DOWN

1 Military camp (Fr.)
2 Ancient Indian
3 Tightly sealed containers: 2 wds.
4 Ending for pistol or haban
5 Have no place to go but up: 3 wds.
6 Win by ___ (barely beat): 2 wds.
7 "The Odd Couple" director
8 Citrus drink
9 Hound
10 Expire
11 "La Femme Nikita" network
12 Bering, e.g.: abbr.
13 D.D.E.'s predecessor
19 What the police need to look through your house: 2 wds.

21 "ER" roles

24 "Married at First Sight" network: 3 wds.

25 "Space Invaders" maker

26 Manicurist's tool: 2 wds.

27 Former Iraqi Deputy Prime Minister Aziz

28 Spring purchase

30 Province of central Spain

32 "Futurama" character with a loopy ponytail

34 "Ready ___ …": 2 wds.

35 Ladies

36 1300 to Nero

43 Never ___ (don't give up): 2 wds.

45 Derek and Jackson

47 Hard work

48 Turner autobiography: 2 wds.

49 Attraction near Orlando

50 Bridges

52 Alphabet series

54 Monthly pub.

55 Chemical suffix

56 Big sizes, briefly

57 Center opening

58 ___ Poke (caramel sucker)

ACROSS

1 French city near the English Channel
5 Food thickeners
10 Poker variety
14 Bicolored ocean prowler
15 City in southern Finland
16 Laura of songwriting
17 At this very moment: 3 wds.
19 Vividly colored fish
20 Big Ten sch.
21 "___ Eat Cake" (Gershwin musical): 2 wds.
22 Alley Oop's wife
23 Make an incision
24 Full of activity
26 Forceful
30 Single-celled aquatic protozoans
34 Roads in France
35 Real heel
37 Promoter of lawlessness, old-style
38 "___ Before Dying": 2 wds.
40 Fruit often dried
42 Make happy
43 Law force
45 O.R. personnel
47 All fired up
48 Guaranteed
50 Regulars
52 Like a shoe
54 CD-___
55 You might burn one for a crush: 2 wds.
58 1901–09 presidential nickname
60 Opposite of masc.
63 An organic compound
64 Capital of Pennsylvania
66 Gull-like bird
67 "___ of Athens" (Shakespeare)
68 Primeval giant of Norse mythology
69 Like Cheerios
70 Incline
71 Gets an eyeful of

DOWN

1 Small silver salmon
2 Lover of Aphrodite
3 Neutral color
4 Not, to a Scot
5 Arising from a common origin
6 Cabinet-level agency responsible for highways, initially
7 Breathlessness while sleeping
8 Floor-cleaning robot
9 Boar's mate
10 It may give you more sleep: 2 wds.
11 Copy editor's bane
12 Russia's ___ Mountains
13 Capital of Qatar
18 Astringent substance
22 Fragile atmosphere layer

1	2	3	4	■	5	6	7	8	9	■	10	11	12	13
14				■	15					■	16			
17				18						■	19			
20			■	21					■	22				
■	■	■	23			■	24		25			■	■	■
26	27	28				29	■	30				31	32	33
34				■	35		36	■	37					
38				39	■	40		41	■	42				
43					44	■	45		46	■	47			
48						49	■	50		51				
■	■	■	52				53	■	54			■	■	■
55	56	57			■	58		59			■	60	61	62
63				■	64						65			
66				■	67					■	68			
69				■	70					■	71			

23 Former name of Muhammad Ali: 2 wds.
25 Thurman of "Dangerous Liaisons"
26 Cover, in a way
27 British Columbia neighbor
28 Sedaka and Armstrong
29 Half-___ (coffee mix): abbr.
31 "Good job!"
32 Be a cast member of: 2 wds.
33 Backyard structures
36 Board member: abbr.
39 New England catch
41 Econ. figure
44 Jellied delicacy
46 Canned fish
49 Particular
51 1992 Robin Williams movie
53 Prefix with -plasty
55 Intermediate: prefix
56 "___ Dinka Doo"
57 Cancel: 2 wds.
59 Bit of rain
60 Show you're mad
61 Ashtabula's lake
62 Team VIPs, shortly
64 Abbr. in some city names
65 Drive-___ (quick touring visits)

23

ACROSS

1 Gear teeth
5 Vigorous dance popular in the 1960s
9 Wonder-worker in India, etc.
14 Take out ___ in the paper (publicize): 2 wds.
15 100 kurus in Turkey
16 ___ acid
17 Clean version of a song: 2 wds.
19 Big name in infomercials
20 Suffix with fact or aster
21 Clinic workers, for short
22 Lightweight wheel
24 Prof.'s helpers
25 City in northern Portugal
27 Cover again with trees
29 "___ Ben Johnson" (inscription on a tomb): 2 wds.
32 ___ manner of speaking: 2 wds.
33 Part inside a tire: 2 wds.
37 Down provider
41 "___ Island", 2008 movie starring Abigail Breslin
42 "Entertainment Tonight" alumna Gibbons
44 Beak
45 Flash of light
47 Eccentric person
49 Poe's "The Narrative of Arthur Gordon ___"
51 ___ bean (source of chocolate)
52 Climbing plant with fragrant flowers: 2 wds.
56 Overwhelm
60 Expression of enlightenment
61 Cape Town country, initially
62 Facing: abbr.
64 D.C.'s nation, for short
65 "___ the Riveter"
67 Route or speed limit indicators: 2 wds.
70 Actress Mitchell, Sister Robin in "Malcolm X"
71 Aqua ___
72 Card balance
73 Serf
74 Snake sound
75 Black-and-white predator

DOWN

1 Chocolate substitute
2 Being broadcast: 2 wds.
3 Italian Modernist poet Carlo Emilio
4 Cold war initials
5 Ran away quickly
6 Clears
7 Geller feller
8 Twista song of 2004: 2 wds.
9 Well advanced in decline: 2 wds.
10 ___, amas, amat …
11 "Roots" subject Kunta ___
12 Ancient Peruvians
13 Perch in a coop
18 Astrologer Sydney
23 Movie-cataloguing grp.
26 Freaks out: 2 wds.
27 Hitchcock movie, or a woman's name
28 Colorful arc seen after a storm

30 Hartsfield-Jackson, on airport tags
31 Cries over
33 Gerund maker
34 Common soccer score
35 "Melody Maker" alternative, initially
36 "The Snowy Day" author ___ Jack Keats
38 ___ double take: 2 wds.
39 New U.S. resident's course, initially
40 Christianity, for one: abbr.
43 N.R.C. forerunner
46 "It's on me!": 2 wds.
48 Narrow-waisted stingers
50 Army cops, initially
52 Actress ___ Michelle Gellar
53 Complete and total
54 Artist's stand
55 O.K. Corral brothers
57 Carpenter's tool
58 "Countdown" airer
59 Edible tubes, e.g.
62 Crew equipment
63 Modern info holders, initially
66 "What was ___ do?": 2 wds.
68 Approval, in Amiens
69 "Indeed ___!": 2 wds.

24

ACROSS

1 Go backpacking
5 Sue Grafton's "___ for Lawless": 2 wds.
8 "Wanted" poster letters
11 Dedicated poems
12 Post, as on a corkboard: 2 wds.
14 Chinese city on the Wei, old-style
15 Webcam or emoticon, e.g.: 2 wds.
18 North Pole toymaker
19 Observer
20 Sacred song
21 ___ pad (kind of tablet)
22 Old Roman port
23 Looks fixedly
25 In place of
26 Plea of being elsewhere
27 Firms: abbr.
28 "Last Action ___" (1993 adventure flick)
32 Chief executive of an organization
36 Aroma
37 Narrow groove
38 Chilly
39 Moisten with water
40 Wealth regarded as an evil influence
42 Bloodsucking she-demon
45 Spreads unchecked
46 Newspaper section: abbr.
47 Nutmeg's coat
48 "A Bridge ___ Far"
51 Studying the forces believe to affect the mind
54 Actual being
55 One of the family
56 Jewish month after Av
57 Place for P.E.
58 Shepherd's setting
59 "Hand it over or ___!"

DOWN

1 Optimist's asset
2 Billy of rock
3 Slit made by cutting or sawing, old-style
4 Abbr. on a city limit sign
5 Content of some closets
6 Chap. 1 preceder
7 Take action against
8 Fish garnish
9 Buddhist principle of causality
10 In addition
12 Check casher
13 Native American infant
14 Attack, as a gnat
16 ___ system
17 Reagan's "Evil Empire" letters
21 ___-toothed tiger

23 Went down in a hurry
24 Greenhorn
25 Driving danger
26 Bustle
27 Oscilloscope part, initially
28 Steering mechanisms for ships
29 As a result
30 Prince's "Purple ___"
31 Getting on
33 Betraying your country
34 At lunch, maybe
35 To wit
39 Accompanying
40 Rattle
41 Deft and active
42 Dissipating energy
43 Deep cavity
44 Cats' prey
45 Indian dignitary
48 Cash register part
49 Taxing load
50 Look at flirtatiously
51 Hard throw, in baseball
52 Be abed
53 Last in a series

25

ACROSS

1 Alpine transport: hyph.
5 Pivot
9 Rockin' Turner
13 Angelic circlet
14 Domino spots
15 Hostile force
17 "___ boy!"
18 Other, to Oswaldo
19 First name in mystery
20 Capricious
22 Burns and Allen, e.g.
23 K-12, in education: hyph.
24 Pope after John X: 2 wds.
25 Merchant vessel officer, briefly
28 Mint, e.g.
30 Ezra Pound work, with "The"
32 Where It.'s at
33 "Hey there!"
37 Dawn on: 2 wds.
39 Comebacks
41 Abandon
42 Summer Games gp.
44 Lawless one
45 Native of the Maritime Provinces of Canada
48 Rueful word
49 Evelyn ___, "Brideshead Revisited" writer
51 Former talk-show host, Jack ___
53 Husband of Pocahontas
54 Turns away
59 Snowbank
60 Asunción assent: 2 wds.
61 Paris airport
62 Binary code representing characters (computing): inits.
63 Blue, in Spain
64 "La Vie en Rose" singer
65 Big top, e.g.
66 Fall mos.
67 Oscar's cousin

DOWN

1 Unfreeze
2 Shower alternative
3 Prefix meaning "height"
4 "... where the buffalo ___"
5 Mar
6 Chinese nut
7 Lift
8 Class for foreigners, for short
9 Cone-shaped home
10 Hotel amenity: 2 wds.
11 Beersheba locale
12 Cremona craftsman
16 2016 and 2017, e.g.: abbr.
21 Casa dweller
24 Decoy or siren, essentially

1	2	3	4	■	5	6	7	8	■	9	10	11	12	■
13				■	14				■	15				16
17				■	18				■	19				
20				21					■	22				
■	■	■	■	23				■	24					■
■	25	26	27		■	28		29				■	■	■
30					31	■	32			■	33	34	35	36
37						38	■	39		40				
41				■	42		43	■	44					
■	■	■	45	46				47	■	48				■
■	49	50				■	51		52		■	■	■	■
53					■	54					55	56	57	58
59					■	60				■	61			
62					■	63				■	64			
■	65				■	66				■	67			

25 "Brandenburg Concertos" composer

26 "___ bitten…"

27 Attractive man, slangily: 2 wds.

29 Big ___, Calif.

30 Fortune 500 listings: abbr.

31 1991 Wimbledon champ Michael

34 Mex. title

35 Holy Fr. women

36 Early role-playing game co., initially

38 Byname for South Africa's Paul Kruger ("Uncle")

40 Beauty queen's crown

43 Overturn (a boat) accidentally

46 "Aha!": 3 wds.

47 Fries topping, often

49 Least satisfactory

50 Girl who visits Wonderland

52 Husks

53 Nutrition amt.

54 Those things, to Antonio

55 "Yup" opposite

56 The ___ Reaper

57 Jack who played Jake in "Big Bad John"

58 Paranormal and fantasy channel

26

ACROSS

1 60 minutes
5 When doubled, a greeting from Mork
9 Indian state near the Himalayas
14 Pretentious phrase of emphasis: 2 wds.
15 Volunteer's words: 2 wds.
16 Turn loose: 2 wds.
17 Diamond Head's setting
18 Put (down)
19 La Junta's county
20 In a hurry: 3 wds.
23 Home planet
24 Perceive
25 ___ Lingus
27 Certain Internet feed
28 Checkup sounds
31 Fungal disease of plants: 2 wds.
34 Cleaned the floor
36 "Common Sense" writer
37 Achieve victory by good luck: 4 wds.
40 Bel ___
42 Kingdom divisions
43 Hardest on the eyes
46 Widow in "Peer Gynt"
47 Judge Lance ___ of the OJ Trial
50 Hi-___, certain LP players
51 180° turn, slangily
53 Actor Bruce
55 1958 movie with Tony Curtis and Sidney Poitier: 3 wds.
60 Motown's original name
61 On or to the left prefix
62 Central point
63 Bothered: 2 wds.
64 Little bit of everything dish
65 "Who Can ___ To", 2014 musical movie: 2 wds.
66 Designer Karan
67 Bismarck's state: abbr., 2 wds.
68 Edible mushrooms

DOWN

1 1978 Burt Reynolds comedy
2 Writer John Henry and fictional character Scarlett
3 Aisle escorts
4 Get out of bed
5 "Cleopatra" backdrop
6 Mil. school
7 Innocents
8 Cause for a downfall
9 "Thanks ___!": 2 wds.
10 Son of Ramses I
11 Sault following?: 2 wds.
12 Mutually accept: 2 wds.
13 Cow's sound
21 Native Algonquin of Oklahoma
22 Auto last made in 1936
26 Road map abbr.

29 New Testament book: abbr.
30 Acquire intelligence
32 Ritzy
33 Bangladesh currency unit
34 Emphatic assent in Acapulco: 2 wds.
35 Available, with "on"
37 Certain Celts
38 Mortgage org.
39 Key town in Arthur C. Clarke's "The City and the Stars"
40 Sta-___ fabric softener
41 Hurried, musically
44 Boy's name in a Johnny Cash title
45 Nonstick stuff
47 Brush aside
48 Prepared for a drive: 2 wds.
49 Mary-Kate and Ashley
52 Intersection sign
54 Charged
56 Dash
57 Brett Spiner character
58 New Balance competitor
59 Small recess
60 Bit

27

ACROSS

1 Literary inits.
4 "I Kissed a Girl" singer Perry
8 Rings (a bell) solemnly
14 City on the Danube
15 ___ Prigogine, Nobel Prize-winning physicist
16 Certain game show decision: 2 wds.
17 Piece of bad advice, slangily: 2 wds.
19 Public speaker
20 Draw air in and out of the lungs
21 100 lb. units
22 G.I. entertainers
23 Impetuousity
27 High-speed Internet inits.
29 Planetary shadow
31 Carbon compound
32 Philosopher Friedrich
34 Singing syllables: hyph.
35 PC bailout key
36 Hallow ending
37 ___ Diego
39 2,000 pounds
40 Ahead by a single point: 2 wds.
42 Being present
45 Philosopher Descartes
46 Bread spreads
47 Coolers, briefly
48 Associated with former times: hyph.
50 Bit of resistance
52 No longer fresh
53 Rotating shaft
57 Rio Grande city: 2 wds.
60 Careless
61 Whistle blower
62 Cleansing agent
63 Document or diet ending
64 John of "A Fish Called Wanda"
65 "My Heart Can't Take ___ More", 1960s hit for The Supremes: 2 wds.
66 City in George R. R. Martin's "A Song of Ice and Fire"

DOWN

1 "Waltz Across Texas" singer Ernest
2 Aspersion
3 Noted plus-size model
4 Caribbean isle St. ___
5 Tavern
6 Chinook salmon
7 Shostakovich's "Babi ___" Symphony
8 ___ thing or two about (has some skill in): 2 wds.
9 Compass point
10 "The Mary Tyler Moore Show" costar: 2 wds.
11 "___ the Good Times Roll"
12 ___-tze (Taoism's founder)
13 Camera inits.
18 Rapid in some rivers
21 Is inclined: 2 wds.

23 President after USG
24 Maternal
25 Congressmen
26 Casual language
27 Quiet down, as rumors or speculation
28 Minute part
30 Rand's mapmaking partner
32 Prefix with surgery or transmitter
33 Zuider ___
34 C&W cable channel
38 Like some famous fables
41 Notorious London prison
43 "Hazel" cartoonist Key
44 Curses
46 At least: 2 wds.
49 Caravan stopping points
51 Thick-skinned African herbivore: abbr.
53 Schedule position
54 Pigeon pea: var.
55 Brightly-colored Australasian parrot
56 Brand of ice cream
57 And others: abbr.
58 "That's 2 funny!"
59 Author of "The Tell-Tale Heart"
60 Fed. assistance program

28

ACROSS

1 Kin of hic or hoc
5 One-time Anaheim Stadium player, briefly: 2 wds.
10 Completely lost
14 ___ other (uniquely): 2 wds.
15 Fine fiddle
16 Action word
17 Capricorn, for one
18 Sci. facilities
19 Prefix with dynamic
20 Unintentional statements supposed to reveal unconscious thoughts: 2 wds.
23 Chinese dynasty circa 2070–1600 BC: var.
24 Lubricate
25 Unlawfully distilled Irish whiskey
28 Spitting sound
30 Carried out
33 Peacemaker Sadat
34 Ending for theater or church
35 Utah's ___ Canyon
36 Make a bit clearer: 4 wds.
39 Rocky peaks
40 Journalist Hamill
41 Hank who hit 755 home runs
42 Made a meal of
43 Swamps
44 Compound with a carbon double bond
45 Vintner's prefix
46 Castaway's home
47 1982 movie starring Meryl Streep: 2 wds.
53 Blowgun ammo
54 Author Marsh
55 Weight used in China and East Asia
57 Former money in Peru
58 More joyful and happy
59 Fertilizer component
60 Money-related: abbr.
61 Animal catcher
62 Cousin of "ahem"

DOWN

1 Experiences
2 "Dream on!": 2 wds.
3 Mech. whiz
4 Alien family on "Saturday Night Live"
5 Kept aside for future use: 2 wds.
6 Membranes in eggs of a bird
7 Scraped (Lat.)
8 Abbr. before a name on an envelope
9 State, capital Jefferson City
10 Good use
11 Drain slowly
12 Goes wrong
13 Blood-typing letters
21 Computer owners
22 52, to Caesar
25 Rotini or rigatoni

26 "… ___ coals," firewalking phrase: 2 wds.
27 Quaint contraction
28 Verse writers
29 Prefix with photo
30 Raison ___
31 "How Can ___?", Freddie Mercury song: 3 wds.
32 John, author of many elegies and sonnets
34 F.B.I. law-enforcement agents: hyph.
35 Disney Channel sitcom: 3 wds.
37 Job seeker's list
38 Winemaker Ernest or Julio
43 Yiddish word of disgust
44 On dry land
45 ___ nerve (eye part)
46 Less cordial
47 One-time bathroom brand, ___-Flush
48 Dog bowl bits
49 Cardinal O'Connor's successor
50 "Don't ___ word": 2 wds.
51 Cadillacs and Chevrolets
52 Wide widths, initially
53 Subtraction amt.
56 Global positioning meas.

29

ACROSS

1 Health resorts
5 Headscarf worn by Muslim women
10 Conclusion
14 Educational inst.
15 Japanese cartoon art
16 Disagreeable obligation
17 "King of the road"
18 They're nuts
19 Castle for Kasparov
20 Tropical South American tree: 2 wds.
23 Euripides drama
24 More tranquil
28 "Without further ___ ..."
29 Dermatology study
33 Strain
34 Observation
36 Assistant
37 Homeland: 2 wds.
41 Dublin's land
42 Couch
43 Two world capital transits
46 Capital on the Dnieper
47 "Frankenstein" setting
50 Opens up, as some jackets
52 Greek poem composed of couplets
54 Like Barack Obama, e.g.: hyph.
58 Lentil-based Indian dish: var.
61 Gastric woe
62 Labels
63 Cry of pain
64 Pieces of money
65 Miscellany
66 Slippery and serpentine
67 Bestow
68 Inert gas

DOWN

1 Outline
2 Shared, as resources
3 Reflective power
4 Area for slaloms
5 Maori war dance
6 Privy to: 2 wds.
7 Dump
8 Accumulate
9 Suit, old-style
10 Bear a reciprocal relation
11 Lennon's love Yoko
12 Batman and Robin, e.g.
13 Demand, as a price
21 Unpleasant to the ear
22 "___ we alone?"
25 Black, as la nuit

26 Mary Baker ___
27 Bread used in a deli
30 Big primate
31 "Dear" ones, sometimes
32 Inverted circumflex
34 Forever
35 100 lisente in Lesotho
37 Appearance
38 Table scraps
39 Arapaho foe
40 Not once
41 Australian non-flyer
44 Clumsy sort
45 Coniferous tree
47 Place
48 Slow movement
49 "Soap" spinoff
51 Sage
53 Climber's spike
55 Battery contents
56 Cafe card
57 Gaelic tongue
58 Salon application
59 Long-handled tool
60 Carpentry tool

30

ACROSS

1 Alchemists' name for mercury
6 1169 erupter
10 Cortex
14 H.H. ___ (Saki)
15 Benefit from planting
16 Hand cream ingredient
17 Document detailing the terms and conditions of compensation: 2 wds.
20 Health regimen
21 Medical research agcy.
22 Bagel choice
23 Dilettante
25 People mentioned in "The Christmas Song"
29 Cry of disgust
30 Guts
31 Bit of slander
33 Little scrap
35 "Dirty" tattletale
36 It's announced by a ringtone: 2 wds.
40 "Don't ___ step farther!": 2 wds.
41 ___ Tomb (solitaire game)
42 A Swiss army knife has lots of them
43 Flavoring obtained from the crocus
46 Supper scrap
47 Places of refuge
48 Exerting an evil influence
52 "I approve the motion"
53 Blemish
54 Ill-mannered
55 Relating to length, breadth, depth and time: hyph.
60 Enthusiastic about
61 Appoint
62 Correct
63 Word with web or pigeon
64 Freudian topics
65 "See ya, señor!"

DOWN

1 Nitrogen compound
2 Dwellers along a tributary of the Little Colorado River
3 Attack
4 Honest
5 Old TV knob, briefly
6 Kovacs or Els
7 Engineering college designation, briefly
8 Glasgow denial
9 Pertinent
10 Monopoly property
11 "American Gladiators" co-host Laila
12 Large mythical bird
13 Lock opener
18 Advance amount
19 Acorn droppers
24 Emerald isle
25 Bob of sausage fame

26 Actress Oberon
27 Certain exams
28 Convened
31 Greek porticoes
32 Having much foliage
33 Dodges socially
34 Flower container
37 Food-poisoning cause
38 Ringlet
39 Small celestial body
40 Govt. purchasing group
44 Salmon fishing tool: 2 wds.
45 Felt bad about
46 Crew members
48 Flowing tresses
49 Toadstools and yeasts, e.g.
50 State bordering Canada
51 People who occupied Britain, Spain and Gaul prior to Roman times
53 In-box item
55 Hale
56 "___! it is an ever-fixed mark": Shak.: 2 wds.
57 Versatile vehicle, for short
58 Glossy publication, for short
59 Author Levin

31

ACROSS

1 1205, to Caesar
5 Legal aide, briefly
9 Impromptu singing style
13 To him in France: 2 wds.
14 Late New York Yankees pitcher Hideki
16 Crater mouths
17 Causes friction
18 Can't take ___ an answer: 2 wds.
19 Actor Novello
20 Dizziness
22 Genetic letters
24 O.K. Corral surname
25 Silent actress Lillian
26 Antipollution org.
29 Measure used in cooking
31 1924 Edna Ferber novel: 2 wds.
33 Conger catcher
35 GI hangouts, initially
37 ___ Sad (capital of Vojvodina)
38 Informal apology: 2 wds.
39 One of the Channel Islands
40 Secluded valleys
42 Actor's goal
43 Hoax: 2 wds.
45 Future ABA member's hurdle
46 "American Composers" author David
47 Grenoble's department
48 Aviation pioneer Post
50 Prime meridian std.
51 ___ es Salaam
52 High schooler
54 Frown
56 Peut-___ (maybe, in Marseilles)
57 Chap, to a Brit.: 2 wds.
60 Food cans, to Brits
63 One of Donald's exes
65 Like some Chardonnay
66 U.S. school near Juarez
67 ___ in the bud: 2 wds.
68 Have ___, try a drink: 2 wds.
69 Like an old grate
70 Narrow street
71 Be inclined

DOWN

1 Basketball Hall-of-Famer Harshman
2 Part of a crossword
3 Newbie interviewer: 2 wds.
4 Long, narrow view
5 Indoor ball game: hyph.
6 Buck addition
7 Battle of Britain grp.
8 Native
9 Hindu titles
10 Early second-century date
11 First of a Latin trio
12 Dungeons & Dragons game co., initially
15 Coffee holders
21 Agcy. concerned with returns
23 Attention-getting cough
25 Submits: 2 wds.

26 Extra effort, figuratively: 2 wds.

27 18th and 19th century artists Rembrandt, Raphaelle, Rubens and Titian

28 Devoted

29 Canine tooth

30 Olympics chant: 2 wds.

32 Cotton pest: 2 wds.

34 Australia's largest lake

36 Competitor to the Heath Bar

41 Star-shaped

44 What remains after deductions, British style

49 10th letter of the Hebrew alphabet

53 Andrews or Brockovich

55 "Das Boot" setting: hyph.

56 Award given by a cable sports station, initially

57 "Bring It ___ It to Win It", 2007 movie starring Ashley Benson: 2 wds.

58 Analogous

59 "Law and Order" grp.

60 River that flows through Mirandela, Portugal

61 That thing's

62 Bk. of the Bible

64 Psychiatrists' org.

32

ACROSS

1 1995 movie about a pig
5 Lacking in Le Havre
9 Plant pores
14 Edible roots
15 Hoof sound
16 Something to talk about
17 Guitarist Lofgren
18 Basilica section
19 Clear, as a disk
20 Not feeling too well: 3 wds.
23 Close female relative: abbr.
24 Flight board letters
25 TV show interruptions
26 Aromatic leaves used in cooking
27 Dark blue
29 "___-ching!"
32 Biblical patriarch
35 Dermatologist's concern
36 Sweet-talk
37 Bolt from the blue: 2 wds.
40 Come together
41 Comic-strip light bulb
42 Ear-related
43 China's Sun Yat-___
44 Cut
45 Flower starter
46 Bro, for one
47 Large mushroom: var.
48 "The Good Shepherd" org.
51 Fundamental concept of economics: 3 wds.
57 Kind of artery or vein
58 Driver's warning
59 Spiced stew of meat and vegetables
60 Natural cavity or hollow in a bone
61 Acknowledge
62 Gadfly, in Britain
63 Get nearer to the end of the day
64 Butts
65 Toy with a tail

DOWN

1 Extra benefit
2 Drupes (of a raspberry, e.g.)
3 Loses hair
4 Be, at the Forum
5 Bad-tempered
6 Part of many stars' names
7 Plane part
8 Vent, as a volcano
9 Stabilize
10 Acts that may bring damages
11 Brightly colored food fish
12 ___-en-scène
13 Maple genus
21 Change, chemically
22 Icicle-forming spots
26 Thai currency

1	2	3	4	■	5	6	7	8	■	9	10	11	12	13
14				■	15				■	16				
17				■	18				■	19				
20				21					22					
23			■	24			■	■	25			■	■	■
■	■	■	26			■	27	28			■	29	30	31
32	33	34			■	35				■	36			
37					38					39				
40				■	41				■	42				
43			■	44				■	45			■	■	■
■	■	■	46			■	■	47			■	48	49	50
51	52	53				54	55				56			
57					■	58				■	59			
60					■	61				■	62			
63					■	64				■	65			

27 Group of nine
28 Lichen component
29 Coarse fiber made into mats
30 Maori war dance
31 ___ Steel ("Guitar Hero" character)
32 Classes
33 ___ function
34 Opposin'
35 Digital music format
36 Unpleasant substance
38 Local protest acronym
39 Brownish gray
44 Lubricant container
45 Moistens with droplets
46 Reserve
47 Software mailing, perhaps: hyph.
48 Hard thickened areas of the skin
49 Coastal feature
50 Oft-repeated dictum
51 Upper layer of the Earth's crust
52 Humerus neighbor
53 Actor Brad
54 Off in the distance
55 ___ Scotia
56 Make fun of

33

ACROSS

1 Spanish hoop
4 National forest in California
10 Fall times: abbr.
14 Computer's storage ability: abbr.
15 Swine enclosure
16 ___ mater (brain part)
17 Lacking the quality or quantity required
19 Bidding site on the Net
20 Ridge of ice on a glacier
21 "___ on my bed my limbs I lay": Coleridge
22 Pub orders
23 Rupture
25 Biblical birthright seller
27 ___-mo
28 F sharp alias
30 "___ first you don't succeed…": 2 wds.
32 Former French coin
35 Skin irritation
36 Super Bowl players, briefly
39 Kind of training
41 Checkers color
43 Japanese beer brand
44 Cub Scout leaders, in the UK
46 Card game start
48 ___-Tiki
49 Track star Jones
50 Urban fantasy novelist Patricia
52 Abilene to Waco dir.
54 Milk: prefix
56 Puffs up
60 Actress Parker of "Superman Returns"
62 Org. for dentists
64 "___ Dark Stranger" (1946 spy film): 3 wds.
65 Res ___ loquitur (law)
66 Place for soldiers captured in war: 2 wds.
68 System of religious belief
69 Rectangular shape
70 Med. care provider
71 1974 CIA spoof movie
72 Small spore-producing plants
73 "Tell ___ Mama" (2009 Norah Jones song)

DOWN

1 Peaceful group in Pennsylvania
2 Actress Taylor of "The Nanny"
3 Big name in astrology
4 For a particular purpose
5 Solitaire game: hyph.
6 Fit of fever
7 Get to the point: 3 wds.
8 Heads of France?
9 Chemistry suffix
10 Frankfurt's river
11 Cut of beef: 2 wds.
12 Fish with a net
13 Final authority: hyph.
18 "Curses!"
22 Spicy chicken dish: 2 wds.

24 Computer key abbr.

26 Department of eastern France

29 From side to side: abbr.

31 Pacino and Gore

32 Govt. agency once headed by Hector Barreto

33 Furniture wood

34 In vain

37 Frat letter

38 Sermon subject

40 U.N. agency for workers

42 "Runaway" singer Shannon

45 "___ man walks into a bar...": 2 wds.

47 ___ Antiqua

51 Fam. tree member

52 Long stories

53 Take in, as a sponge: 2 wds.

55 ___-loading (pre-athletics activity)

57 Patrick, senator from Vermont

58 "___ at 'em!"

59 Taste of a substance

61 Consumes

63 Those, to José

66 Small dog: abbr.

67 Number of even primes

34

ACROSS

1 Chase of "Now, Voyager"
5 Flu symptom
9 Major League Baseball player Brian
14 Former Chinese monetary unit
15 ___ sum (Chinese flowering cabbage)
16 Gas meter measure
17 Harvard and Princeton are part of it: 2 wds.
19 In ___ (lab-grown)
20 Build (on)
21 Fisherman's pole
23 Beef fat used in cooking
24 Fine fiddle maker
27 After a fashion: 3 wds.
29 Symbol of the Soviet Union: 2 wds.
32 Professional parker
33 Take ___ from (learn something): 2 wds.
34 Brain, in slang
37 Thrilling: hyph.
42 Cravat pin: var.
43 Palindromic time
45 Extend a subscription
48 Fail to have the desired effect
50 Fort's defense
53 Alpine call
54 Portray
55 1920 science fiction play
56 Maker: abbr.
57 Fibber's confession: 2 wds.
59 Hamburger with cheese: 2 wds.
64 Big name in mints
65 Berkshire school
66 Air France airport
67 All in ___ work: 2 wds.
68 Column crossers
69 Bills

DOWN

1 "Lord, is ___?": Matthew
2 Washroom, briefly
3 Janitor's jangler
4 Totally disorganized: 3 wds.
5 Part of U.S.N.A.: abbr.
6 Bill amt.
7 Nymph of the Muslim paradise
8 "___ America" (CBS News): 2 wds.
9 Cable channel
10 Carpentry tool
11 Adjust, in a way
12 A cop might put someone under it
13 Be theatrical
18 Correct one's work
22 Mona Lisa painter
24 Constellation near Scorpius

25 Kind of engr.

26 "For two," on sheet music: 2 wds.

28 Bank deposit

30 Pacifist

31 Lassoer's cord

35 Caught

36 Largest Mariana Island

38 AAA recommendations: abbr.

39 Sell out, in a way: 2 wds.

40 Reason to be turned away by a bouncer: 2 wds.

41 Clinton's #2

44 First word of Dante's "Inferno"

45 Fulminated

46 Mark Twain's New York hometown

47 Between eighty and one hundred

49 "Three Inches" channel

50 Skin fold

51 Con artist

52 A Muse

56 Geographical features, for short

58 Grad. degree

60 Haul

61 "___ pales in Heaven the morning star": Lowell

62 Degree for an att.

63 Athletes Cobb and Warner

35

ACROSS

1 Kilmer of "Batman Forever"
4 Kind of cracker
10 Marcel Marceau persona
13 Bundle
14 "It'd be my pleasure": 2 wds.
15 ___ gratia artis
16 Yankees' #13, to fans: hyph.
17 "A Midsummer Night's Dream" role
18 ___ Moines, Iowa
19 Island south of the Malay Peninsula
21 Cruise of "Mission: Impossible III"
23 Mend a seam
24 Clogs' cousins
27 Big deal
28 Gardner of "On the Beach"
31 Fallen apart
32 Mechanically operated instrument
34 "Look no further!": 2 wds.
35 "Incorrect!": 3 wds.
38 Nicely organized
39 ___ Court
40 Against the law
42 Ending for Power or lemon
43 Not morning: abbr.
46 Hugh of magazine fame
47 10th president of the US
49 AOL alternative
50 Not rocket science: 3 wds.
54 Ghost word
56 Easy to control
58 Aquarium
59 I love, in Latin class
60 Financial arrangement involving a neutral third party
61 Gospels follower
62 "___ and Stimpy"
63 Places to sleep
64 Court people, for short

DOWN

1 Diverse
2 "The Tempest" king
3 Climber's respite
4 Amorphous food
5 Film lead-in for Cop
6 Say it's so
7 In this place
8 ___ Z: 2 wds.
9 Fireman-hero Guy of "Fahrenheit 451"
10 Speak unfavorably about: hyph.
11 Extreme anger
12 Endings to some e-mails, initially
13 Port in southeast Iraq
20 Anticipate
22 Accommodate

■	1	2	3	■	4	5	6	7	8	9	■	10	11	12
13				■	14						■	15		
16				■	17						■	18		
19				20					■	21	22		■	■
23					■	■	■	■	24				25	26
27			■	28	29	30	■	31						
■	■	■	32				33			■	34			
■	35	36								37				■
38				■	39							■	■	■
40				41			■	42			■	43	44	45
46						■	■	■	■	47	48			
■	■	49			■	50	51	52	53					
54	55		■	56	57					■	58			
59			■	60						■	61			
62			■	63						■	64			■

24 Caught

25 Assay or essay, perhaps

26 Military inits.

29 ___ Clements, the "Father of Hillbilly Jazz"

30 Declare legally void

31 Extremely

32 Communion plates

33 V.T. Hamlin character, Alley ___

35 Distant: prefix

36 Henry Hudson's ship: 2 wds.

37 "…___ man with seven wives…": 3 wds.

38 U.S. medical research agcy.

41 Male or female

43 Animal prized for its wool

44 Bluffs

45 Arduous journeys

48 Swedish seaport on the Baltic

50 ___ Domani (wine brand)

51 Broadcasts

52 Groove

53 Trees used to make archery bows

54 Block passage through

55 Cockney residence

57 Bilbao bear

36

ACROSS

1 Open ___ of worms: 2 wds.
5 Fig. on a car sticker
9 First governor of Alaska
13 Play ___ (perform alone): 2 wds.
14 Shimmering aquarium fish
15 Green in Grenoble
16 ___ Antoinette
17 "Every ___ King", autobiography of Huey Long, Governor of Louisiana: 2 wds.
18 Rest stop, once
19 Information holders stored alphabetically: 2 wds.
21 "Los Olvidados" director Buñuel
22 Medical research agcy.
23 Fixed in one's purpose: 2 wds.
25 Sore spots
30 "Letters from ___ Jima" (2006 film)
31 Harvest goddess
32 Aussie jumpers
34 Second-grade sequence, initially
38 Deceitful person: 4 wds.
42 "No Strings Attached" band
43 "Ripley's Believe ___ Not": 2 wds.
44 Channel owned by DirecTV and Sony Pictures Television: inits.
45 Channels 14 through 83, initially
47 Freedom of access: 2 wds.
50 Passed, as laws
54 Average grade
55 Either of the two grooves in an archery bow
56 Deteriorates through neglect: 3 wds.
62 12th month of the Jewish civil year
63 "Once ___ a time…"
64 ___ de Mayo
65 Buddy
66 On or to the left prefix
67 Come about
68 Hydrocarbon suffixes
69 Prepare for print
70 Dissents

DOWN

1 Dumb-ox connector: 2 wds.
2 128 cubic feet
3 Creatures from outer space
4 "Hell is other people" play: 2 wds.
5 N.Y.C. cultural center
6 Bandy words
7 Science and technology dept. of a co.: 3 wds.
8 First stage of an operation: 2 wds.
9 Bad person
10 Biology classification
11 "L.A. Law" lawyer
12 Explosive experiment: abbr., 2 wds.
13 "What Kind of Fool ___?": 2 wds.
20 French dear

24 Like gossiping tongues
25 Rigging pro
26 Hosp. staffers
27 "___, old chap": 2 wds.
28 Rice-a-___
29 ___ voce
33 Boutique
35 "Othello" fellow
36 ___ buco
37 Mil. backup group
39 Fist joints
40 Rhinelander's "real"
41 Build
46 Switch once used to punish children
48 Reader of "The Weekly Standard", perhaps
49 "Bicycle Thieves" director Vittorio: 2 wds.
50 Purgative
51 Actor Lloyd ___
52 Critical
53 Deceived
57 ___ Sad (capital of Vojvodina)
58 Rotten little kid
59 Suffix with consist or depend
60 Old French coins
61 Palme ___ (Cannes award)

37

ACROSS

1 Be a downer
5 Debatable
9 Scolded
13 Balanced
14 Jewish calendar's sixth month
15 In a lather: 2 wds.
17 Vast plain and National Park in Tanzania
19 Bulging jars
20 "Mustache Hat" artist Jean
21 Give it ___ (try out): 2 wds.
22 Disease-causing organisms
24 Crushes underfoot: 2 wds.
26 "___us a son..."
27 The item specified
28 Greek portico
29 ___ Poly
32 Christmas ___
34 For the moment
36 Arabian Peninsula country
37 Attention
38 Food for Fido
39 To the letter
42 Crazies south of the border
43 Live and breathe
44 They give people big heads
45 In ___ of (for)
46 Carbo-loader's fare, slangily
47 Infantile
50 Knight in shining armor
53 Rocky Mountain Indian
54 Possible roll of the die
55 To no ___ (fruitlessly)
56 Butt of a prank played on a certain date: 2 wds.
59 Early copters
60 Cardinal
61 Artificial bait
62 Part of a script
63 A year in Italy
64 Broken in

DOWN

1 Flat-topped lands
2 Blatant
3 Commit
4 Chemistry suffix
5 Larva of a fly
6 Cineplex ___ (cinema chain)
7 Feedbag morsel
8 Small river, often
9 Southern tribe
10 Big name in wireless
11 "___ all come out in the wash"
12 ___-purpose (having two uses)

1	2	3	4	■	5	6	7	8	■	9	10	11	12	■
13				■	14				■	15				16
17				18					■	19				
20			■	21			■	22	23					
24			25				■	26				■	■	■
■	■	27				■	28				■	29	30	31
32	33				■	34					35			
36				■	■	37			■	■	38			
39				40	41				■	42				
43			■	44				■	45				■	■
■	■	■	46				■	47					48	49
50	51	52					■	53			■	54		
55					■	56	57				58			
59					■	60				■	61			
■	62				■	63				■	64			

16 Last Greek consonant
18 Like the "ng" sound
23 At another time
25 Make a call
28 Elite U.S. Navy squad
29 Winding
30 Choir member
31 Diminished by
32 Bubbly drink
33 Mideast ruler: var.
34 Extravagant theatrical piece
35 Bunk
40 Drive back
41 Malarial fever
42 Slander's cousin
45 Barrio resident
46 Offshoot
47 Engraver's tool
48 Cursed
49 ___ up (hid out)
50 Dusting cloth
51 Demonic
52 Indian dress
57 Criticize harshly
58 Winter bug

38

ACROSS

1 Guam's capital, old-style
6 Spanish uncles
10 P.D.Q., in memos
14 Shot a certain spray at
15 "Ignorance ___ excuse!": 2 wds.
16 Boys
17 Cuisine of a very high standard: 2 wds.
19 Les États-___
20 Artful
21 "How the Other Half Lives" author
22 Simple type of plane engine
24 "___ 18" (Leon Uris novel)
25 Inauspicious
26 Glossy fabrics
29 Brain casings
30 Actor Sulkin, Liam Booker of "Faking It"
31 Suffix with harde- or wilde-
32 Dynasty during which much of the Great Wall of China was built
35 "Ah, me!"
36 God, to Muslims
37 ___ fever: 2 wds.
38 Campus women's org.
39 Composed
40 Traditional coronation place of most French kings
41 Nova follower
43 Poem of fourteen 10- or 11-syllable lines
44 Academic type
46 ___-daisy: hyph.
47 Homework eater, supposedly: 2 wds.
48 Ale or coffee
49 "Zip-A-Dee-Doo-___"
52 "___ Three Lives" (1950s TV drama): 2 wds.
53 Vanilla Ice hit: 3 wds.
56 Unit of weight in some Muslim countries
57 "Lovely" Beatles girl
58 Sued, old-style
59 Zaire's Mobutu ___ Seko
60 Jacob's first wife
61 Old "Hollywood Squares" regular

DOWN

1 Some movie theaters, initially
2 Wilde's "The Ballad of Reading ___"
3 "___ From Within", 2014 horror movie: 2 wds.
4 ABC News reporter Potter
5 Like fans
6 Leg bone
7 Small land masses: abbr.
8 Low digit
9 Blended whiskey: 2 wds.
10 Grads of a school
11 Largest river of central California: 2 wds.
12 French farewell
13 Attention-getting sounds
18 Lagerlöf's "The Wonderful Adventures of ___"
23 Aretha Franklin's "___ No Way"

1	2	3	4	5	■	6	7	8	9	■	10	11	12	13
14					■	15				■	16			
17					18					■	19			
20			■	21				■	22	23				
■	■	■	24				■	25						
26	27	28				■	29						■	■
30					■	31					■	32	33	34
35				■	36					■	37			
38			■	39					■	40				
■	■	41	42					■	43					
44	45						■	46				■	■	■
47						■	48				■	49	50	51
52				■	53	54					55			
56				■	57				■	58				
59				■	60				■	61				

24 Russian fighter planes
25 Companion of Artemis
26 Campus orgs.
27 "Alice's Restaurant" singer Guthrie
28 Perforated pages in magazines, etc.: 2 wds.
29 Late "Queen of Salsa" ___ Cruz
31 Former British P.M. Tony
33 "You've Got a Friend ___": 2 wds.
34 Vogue and Vanity Fair publisher Condé ___
36 Expression of encouragement to a woman
37 Actress Sofer
39 Without help
40 New Mexico's "Area 51" site
42 Pamper
43 Design criterion, briefly
44 Mixes up
45 "Daphnis et ___"
46 Dickens character ___ Heep
48 ___ carotene
49 Arise
50 Not up
51 Jekyll's alter ego
54 Inc., in Paris
55 Dark horse

39

ACROSS

1 Not in any danger
5 Entrées in shells
10 Trans-Siberian Railroad city
14 Chem. ending
15 Sealed glass capsule containing a liquid
16 The "B" of N.B.
17 Tired of life: 2 wds.
19 "And a lot of others besides that": 2 wds.
20 "Platoon" setting, for short
21 Press into service
22 Overhead
23 Lacking formality
28 Divided
30 Dorm annoyance
31 Bog mosses used as fuel
32 Missouri's state tree
36 Money before a poker hand
37 Saline
39 Rock climber's challenge
41 Bootlicking
43 Stocking lines
44 Discharge
46 "___ bet?"
47 Making a supposition
52 Zingers
53 "Nightmare" street
54 (The) Union, familiarly
57 Akron's home
58 Typesetter
62 Relocate
63 Be in store for
64 Astronaut's insignia letters
65 Men-to-be
66 Indiana's state flower
67 Door opener

DOWN

1 Darned, say
2 Relative of the buffalo
3 Devise (a plan, for example)
4 Addition
5 Leather strap
6 Foreign heads of state: var.
7 Book balancer, briefly
8 Owned by you and me
9 Foxy
10 Old manuscript markings
11 Copycat's phrase: 2 wds.
12 Big mess
13 Salmon after they have spawned
18 Channels
22 From the start
24 Fertilizer component
25 Infinite

1	2	3	4	■	5	6	7	8	9	■	10	11	12	13
14				■	15					■	16			
17				18						■	19			
20			■	21			■	■	■	22				
■	■	23	24				25	26	27					
28	29				■	30					■	■	■	■
31					■	■	32				33	34	35	■
36				■	37	38				■	39			40
■	41			42				■	■	43				
■	■	■	■	44				45	■	46				
47	48	49	50						51				■	■
52					■	■	■	53			■	54	55	56
57				■	58	59	60				61			
62				■	63					■	64			
65				■	66					■	67			

26 Not worth debating

27 Wild party

28 Bath bath

29 Writing implements

33 Huge sea

34 Large ape with long red hair: hyph.

35 Consign to the underworld

37 Long, deep breath

38 Away from the wind

40 Govt. property manager

42 Docs for dogs, maybe

43 Moves through water

45 Haberdashery item: 2 wds.

47 Nuclear weapon: hyph.

48 Popular search engine

49 In on (with "to")

50 Woodwind instruments

51 100 groszy in Poland

55 Barely passable: hyph.

56 Middle Easterner, often

58 Toothpaste tube topper

59 Be indebted to

60 Cultural Revolution leader

61 Printer cartridge contents

40

ACROSS

1 Truck manufacturer located in Tulsa, Oklahoma, initially
4 Fink
8 Basin for holy water
13 Former Vietnamese coin
14 Palestinian Islamic movement
16 Bit of statuary
17 Bookmarked address, briefly
18 Of ___ (somewhat): 2 wds.
19 Exclamation of frustration: 2 wds.
20 Checks the totals again
22 County seat in Crow Wing County, Minnesota
24 Undesirable effect in flash photography: hyph.
25 Tidal bore
26 "___ unrelated note … ": 2 wds.
27 Waterproof canvases
29 ___ Perignon champagne
32 Song's beginning: abbr.
34 Footwear items
36 Certain player in a knockout competition: hyph.
41 Big name in computer printers
42 Charger
43 Dry, as wine
44 "The Other Day ___ Bear", traditional campfire song: 3 wds.
46 Area of NYC
50 Israeli desert
52 Join forces: 2 wds.
54 Short, ribbed pasta
57 Div. for Padres and Giants: 2 wds.
58 Avoid
59 More cunning
61 Tuna of the Pacific
62 Cartoon cat
63 Frank Sinatra song "It's ___ New to Me": 2 wds.
64 Sleep clinic study, for short
65 Ireland's patron, for short: 2 wds.
66 Effortless
67 Solid ___ rock: 2 wds.

DOWN

1 Sweet Spanish snack
2 Veer wildly
3 Pina ___, popular cocktail
4 Sheltered from light or heat
5 Car stereo input
6 I love: Lat.
7 Rossini work: 3 wds.
8 Part of a flight
9 Oscar-winning screenwriter Robert
10 ""Him ___ – What's It Gonna Be?" Paul Revere & the Raiders song: 2 wds.
11 Org. for part-time soldiers
12 Pool
15 Watch part
21 Actor in "GoodFellas" and "Raging Bull"

1	2	3	■	4	5	6	7	■	■	8	9	10	11	12
13			■	14				15	■	16				
17			■	18					■	19				
20			21			■	22		23					
24						■	25					■	■	■
26				■	27	28				■	■	29	30	31
■	■	■	32	33				■	■	34	35			
36	37	38						39	40					
41					■	■	42					■	■	■
43			■	■	44	45				■	46	47	48	49
■	■	■	50	51				■	52	53				
54	55	56						■	57					
58					■	59		60			■	61		
62					■	63					■	64		
65					■	■	66				■	67		

23 Lynch, Holder and Mukasey, initially
28 Airport abbr.
29 601 in Roman numerals
30 Approves
31 Phoenix hrs.
33 Mathematician's ordinal
34 Freelancer's enc.
35 Familiar saying: 2 wds.
36 NOP followers
37 Quick turnaround, slangily
38 Banking abbr.
39 One of the Addams family
40 Tidy trait
44 Billy Joel's "___ to Extremes": 2 wds.
45 Organization for the supersmart
47 Golfer Mark
48 Quietens
49 Most favorable conditions
50 Gymnast Comaneci
51 Kindle material: hyph.
53 N.F.L. Hall-of-Famer Hirsch
54 Officiates: abbr.
55 "Why did ___ him go?": 2 wds.
56 Swallow greedily
60 Dockworker's org.

ACROSS

1 "Sweet Dreams" star Jessica
6 ___ voce: softly
11 Toronto media inits.
14 Endured
15 Happy ___ be: 2 wds.
16 "___ la la!"
17 System of complementary medicine
19 Early gangsta rap collective
20 Reggae singer Peter
21 Chemist's suffix
22 Demeanor
24 "___, drink, and be merry"
26 Part of a religious title
27 Short-term blocking of sunlight: 2 wds.
33 Hawkins of "Treasure Island"
34 Map within a map
35 "This must weigh ___!": 2 wds.
36 Legislate
38 F.D.R. plan
39 Instruct
40 Payment for a road
41 Processed foods manufacturer
43 Great Plains Indian
44 Jewelry store purchase: 2 wds.
48 Caribbean cruise stop
49 Suffix with Ecuador
50 Send down a notch in rank
52 Island north of Santorini
54 Lose color
58 Suffix with fib or fist
59 Honest person: hyph.
62 Assembled
63 St. ___ fire
64 Actress Kelly
65 Amiens soul
66 Printing copy: abbr.
67 "___ to Break Free", Queen song: 2 wds.

DOWN

1 Future atty.'s exam
2 Warner Music Group record label
3 Entre ___
4 Ground squirrel
5 College URL ender
6 Bursae
7 Bone in comb. form
8 Southwest campus, initially
9 Landing spot for a plane
10 Common tie score, in baseball or soccer: 2 wds.
11 Display of bad temper
12 Boxer Riddick
13 Burn slightly
18 Out: 2 wds.
23 Water nymph
25 Arguing: 2 wds.

26 Hold back

27 Assign to, as blame: 2 wds.

28 Blend

29 Breathing problem

30 Embankment

31 Sound heard twice in "ginger": 2 wds.

32 Greek war goddess

33 Ballet burst

37 Humidor item

39 Biblical prophet

42 Explosive experiment: abbr., 2 wds.

45 Rain channel

46 Glenn Miller Band vocalist Ray

47 Fresh water entering a lake, e.g.

50 Russian legislature

51 Kind of school: abbr.

52 "Ripley's Believe ___ Not": 2 wds.

53 Quite: 2 wds.

55 Et ___

56 Actress Laura of "Rambling Rose"

57 Q.E.D. part

60 "Yer out!" shouter, shortly

61 Brit. former record label

42

ACROSS

1 "Relax, and that's an order!": 2 wds.
7 Brit. honors
11 Extinct flightless bird
14 Arm and upper body exercise: hyph.
15 "___ Rock", Simon and Garfunkel hit: 3 wds.
16 Hosp. dept.
17 Government in power
18 Legionary insects: 2 wds.
20 "___, That Kiss" (1931 song)
21 Computer storage area
23 Handheld CPUs
24 Ball raiser
26 Farm female
27 Garlic mayonnaise
28 Went in
31 Arthur Miller's fictional salesman
33 Helgenberger of "CSI"
34 Metrical unit of two feet
36 Hectic hosp. sections
39 "___ corny as Kansas...": 2 wds.
40 Last-minute greeting: hyph.
41 "___ any wonder?": 2 wds.
42 Case guy, for short
43 Scarcely detectable amount
44 Org. with a "Shelter of the Week" award
45 Fashion designer Donna
47 Short solos
49 Courtroom statements
51 ___ Arbor
53 ___ lab letters
54 Certain food stores, initially
55 Prophet in the Second Book of Kings
57 Japanese computer company, shortly
60 Mr. Bonaparte
62 "___ Fall in Love", Jean Terrell album: 3 wds.
64 Coll. senior's test
65 "___ Brockovich"
66 Rotation-producing force
67 C.I.A. precursor
68 ___-poly
69 Invites to enter: 2 wds.

DOWN

1 Peak or tip: prefix
2 "The Cosby Show" boy
3 Multi-recording media, once: hyph, 2 wds.
4 What a "Wheel of Fortune" contestant might buy: 2 wds.
5 Warmest season of the year
6 Fencer's blade
7 Cat's sound: var.
8 Calliope cousins: 2 wds.
9 Oscar's cousin
10 Put into words
11 Be watchfully accurate and punctilious: 5 wds.

1	2	3	4	5	6	■	7	8	9	10	■	11	12	13
14						■	15				■	16		
17						■	18				19			
20			■	21		22				■	23			
■	■	24	25		■	26			■	27				
28	29				30		■	31	32				■	■
33				■	34		35				■	36	37	38
39				■	40					■	41			
42			■	43						■	44			
■	■	45	46				■	47		48				
49	50				■	51	52		■	53			■	■
54				■	55				56		■	57	58	59
60				61				■	62		63			
64			■	65				■	66					
67			■	68				■	69					

12 Based on base eight
13 Also, in Angoulême
19 Samoan port
22 Castor, e.g.: 2 wds.
25 Lines of thought, initially?
27 Former First Daughter Carter
28 Discharge
29 April or May
30 Root rot
32 Harder to explain
35 Hippie's hangout
37 "Little Caesar" role
38 Train stops: abbr.
41 "The heat ___!": 2 wds.
43 AARP members, briefly
46 Facetious "I see": 2 wds.
48 Some potatoes
49 ___ Boingo, "Deadman's Party" band
50 Lab gels
52 Silly goose
55 Architect Saarinen who designed the Tulip Chair
56 ___ snag (got stuck): 2 wds.
58 Needle holder
59 "The Big Lebowski" director
61 Celtic Neptune
63 Biblical boat

43

ACROSS

1 Bay
5 Certain Internet feeds, initially
9 According to: 2 wds.
14 Play ___ (tennis): 2 wds.
15 Play to ___, draw: 2 wds.
16 "___ of Two Cities", novel by Charles Dickens: 2 wds.
17 Brake element
18 Table d'___
19 Plant also known as bugle
20 Travels about: 2 wds.
23 Fetid, rank
24 Do it wrong
25 Computer that sang "Daisy"
26 Close in time: 2 wds.
28 "___, right"
30 "... women do ___ require?", Blake: 2 wds.
32 Prefix for sphere or cycle
34 Nozzle
35 BBC rival
38 All-encompassing endorsement: 2 wds.
42 Suffix with ball or buff
43 Goddess of peace
44 Type of flower cluster
45 Director Kurosawa
46 Enthusiasm
48 Putrefied
51 Constricting snake
52 Daughter of Hyperion
55 Downsizer
56 Bruce Willis film: 2 wds.
60 Territory off China's coast
62 Schoolmarmish
63 Lambs: Lat.
64 Voting groups
65 Frankie Avalon's "___ Dinah"
66 Bird feeder favorite
67 In a daze: 2 wds.
68 Not yet repaid
69 Towel inscription

DOWN

1 Sponge
2 Tree that provides wickers
3 Brit. church officer
4 List enders, briefly
5 Enthusiastic: hyph.
6 Bar seat
7 In ___ (where found)
8 Glimpsed
9 Bond initial rating from Moody's
10 Apostle whose feast day is December 27th: 2 wds.
11 Abdul of "American Idol"
12 The British Museum's ___ Marbles
13 Tot up again
21 "I have the answer!"
22 Block, as a river: 2 wds.

1	2	3	4	■	5	6	7	8	■	9	10	11	12	13
14				■	15				■	16				
17				■	18				■	19				
20				21					22	■	23			
24			■	25			■	■	26	27				
■	■	28	29			■	30	31				■	■	■
32	33			■	■	34					■	35	36	37
38				39	40						41			
42			■	43					■	■	44			
■	■	■	45					■	46	47			■	■
48	49	50				■	■	51			■	52	53	54
55				■	56	57	58				59			
60				61	■	62				■	63			
64					■	65				■	66			
67					■	68				■	69			

27 Four: prefix
29 Hamburger's one
30 Classic toothpaste brand
31 Yep's opposite
32 Big inits. in movies
33 "Xanadu" band, for short
34 Ending for gang or young
35 Columbia and Yale are part of it: 2 wds.
36 Glaswegian's cap
37 Nationals grp.
39 Hall-of-Famer Cuyler
40 Author Segal
41 South American wood sorrel
45 Disappear without ___: 2 wds.
46 Rocketed
47 Suffix with Caesar
48 Ballroom beat
49 Elevate
50 Cowboy ___ Bill
51 45 rpm record half: hyph.
53 Dog's master
54 Sketches
57 Beehive, e.g.
58 Sketched
59 ___ browns (breakfast food)
61 Explorer Johnson

ACROSS

1 Brace used for fastening things together
6 Make bigger, as a photo: abbr.
9 Saharan sanctuary
14 Romero of the screen
15 Kiwi's late kin
16 One of Columbus's ships
17 Plant fiber used for nets and cordage
18 Nomadic
20 Individually
22 Cold cubes
23 These may be inflated
24 Sought approval by fawning: 2 wds.
28 Part of military addresses, initially
29 Camera type, briefly
30 Asian language
31 Pay stub abbr.
34 Buckwheat pancake
36 Gangster's gun, for short
38 ___ more (several): 2 wds.
40 Completely irrational, colloquially: 5 wds.
44 Military camp (Fr.)
45 Medical research agcy.
46 Dadaist artists Jean and Hans
47 "Regnava ___ silenzio" (aria from "Lucia di Lammermoor")
48 Absorb, as an expense
51 ___-mo camera
53 Aegean tourist mecca
54 Winter Olympics sport: hyph.
57 Robert who played A.J. Soprano
60 London's ___ Gardens
61 Clapton on guitar
62 Celebrity
65 Conductor Zubin
68 "Princess Mononoke" genre
69 Home of the Mustangs, initially
70 ___ the hole: 2 wds.
71 "One Flew Over the Cuckoo's Nest" novelist
72 Cologne cooler
73 Bird houses

DOWN

1 201, in Roman numerals
2 Bandleader Brown
3 Concerning certain space rocks
4 Of the cheekbone
5 Concise summary
6 Former long-time record label initials
7 ___, but when: 2 wds.
8 Like some church matters
9 Unlock, poetically
10 Clothes-drying frame
11 Catch
12 "Give ___ further thought!": 2 wds.
13 Some srs. take them
19 Gulf of Finland feeder
21 Hägar the Horrible's honey

24 Taxi drivers, at times
25 Burning the midnight oil: 2 wds.
26 Apothecary's weight
27 "Amazing!"
31 Seven ___: 2 wds.
32 Lethargy
33 Formal, casually
35 Afternoon snooze
37 Lay out in the sun
39 FDR home loan org.
41 Forecaster
42 Specialized computer, for short
43 Daphnis's love
49 Approvals, slangily: hyph.
50 Sleeping sickness carrier
52 "___ in New Orleans", Al Hirt jazz album of 1963: 2 wds.
54 ___ de menthe
55 Hindu religious teacher
56 Nephew's sister
57 "Out of Africa" author Dinesen
58 French moonlight: clair de ___
59 Like some churches: abbr.
63 Benjamin's "Law & Order" role
64 Ukr. neighbor
66 Black-throated ___ (Asian bird)
67 Ques. response

ACROSS

1 Greek letter
5 Compulsion
9 Dictionary abbr.
12 Marlin or Cardinal, e.g.
13 Frequent guest on "The Love Boat"
14 Baseball's Tony or Alejandro
15 Skin: suffix
16 Big name in supplemental insurance
17 Garden decorations
18 Defrauds
20 Joins forces: 2 wds.
22 Biscotti flavoring
24 Deviation from the norm
25 Triple
27 Manage, with "out"
28 Darth's daughter
29 Aunts in la familia
31 7th-century BC Greek city
35 Valuable stone
36 Choir voice
38 Salt Lake City hrs.
39 Popular Japanese beer
42 Gull-like bird
43 ___-daisy: hyph.
44 Small: suffix
46 ___ grip (wrestling hold)
48 Back part: 2 wds.
52 Baltimore's ___ Harbor
53 Acting, in a way: 2 wds.
54 Put a stop to
57 "Cave Bear" chronicler Jean
58 Boxer Ali
61 Gutter site
62 Algonquian language
63 Not able to serve, as with the military
64 Barbershop sound
65 Common contraction
66 Audition
67 "Let it stand"

DOWN

1 Visiting the U.S. Capitol, say: 2 wds.
2 Hot roll topper
3 Italian verse form: 2 wds.
4 Country, capital Yerevan
5 VHF's counterpart
6 State capital of North Carolina: abbr.
7 Persona non ___
8 Second epoch of the Tertiary period
9 Vice ___
10 Invalidate
11 Grating
13 "The Child's Bath" painter Mary
14 Beat

19 Diarist Anaïs
21 Golfer Isao ___
23 Great Lakes tribesmen
25 Concert souvenirs, for short
26 N.Y. squad, familiarly
28 N.Y.C. airport
30 Sans ___ (carefree): Fr.
32 Significant
33 Large nation letters, once
34 1959 Kingston Trio hit
37 Head protector: 2 wds.
40 Rush violently
41 Intestinal parts
43 Of no value
45 Overgorge
47 Snow, in Scotland
48 ___ Motel, pest bait device
49 Accustom: var.
50 Thoreau work, "Faith in ___": 2 wds.
51 Early American diplomat Silas
55 1960s–70s singer Sands
56 Part of U.S.D.A.: abbr.
59 Conditions
60 Fired up

46

ACROSS

1 Torso, slangily
4 Ladybug features
9 Online issue: hyph.
13 Letters accompanying some 2,000-year-old+ dates
14 Get ready to drive: 2 wds.
15 ___ citato
16 Temporary insurance certificate: 2 wds.
18 Deride: 2 wds.
19 Central point
20 They may be hailed: 2 wds.
22 Use a key on a door
23 "South Park" kid with a two-part head
24 Ad ___ (improvise)
25 Likewise
26 "Star Trek: Voyager" character
28 Deny
31 Early Dadaist works
33 Spanish chant: 2 wds.
36 Court case standout: 2 wds.
40 Blissful
41 Company dept.
44 African antelopes
47 ___ and haw (stall)
50 Road reversal, familiarly
51 Kay Kyser's "___ Reveille"
52 Perry Mason creator's initials
55 Spheres
57 Cherish: 2 wds.
60 Toothbrush brand: 2 wds.
61 Get used (to)
62 Footwear securers
65 Furniture wood
66 AM/FM device
67 Gallery objects
68 Multitude
69 Make a measure
70 Sony handheld device, initially

DOWN

1 World Service provider
2 Reagan Supreme Court nominee
3 Evolves
4 Hit
5 U-Haul rival
6 Fair-hiring agcy.
7 "___ Frutti" (Little Richard hit)
8 Say words
9 Cast-of-thousands film
10 Silver, tin, etc.
11 "Lawrence of ___"
12 Copes: 2 wds.
15 "___ believe in yesterday": 2 wds.
17 Skeleton prefix
21 Arc lamp gas
22 Tony winner Hagen

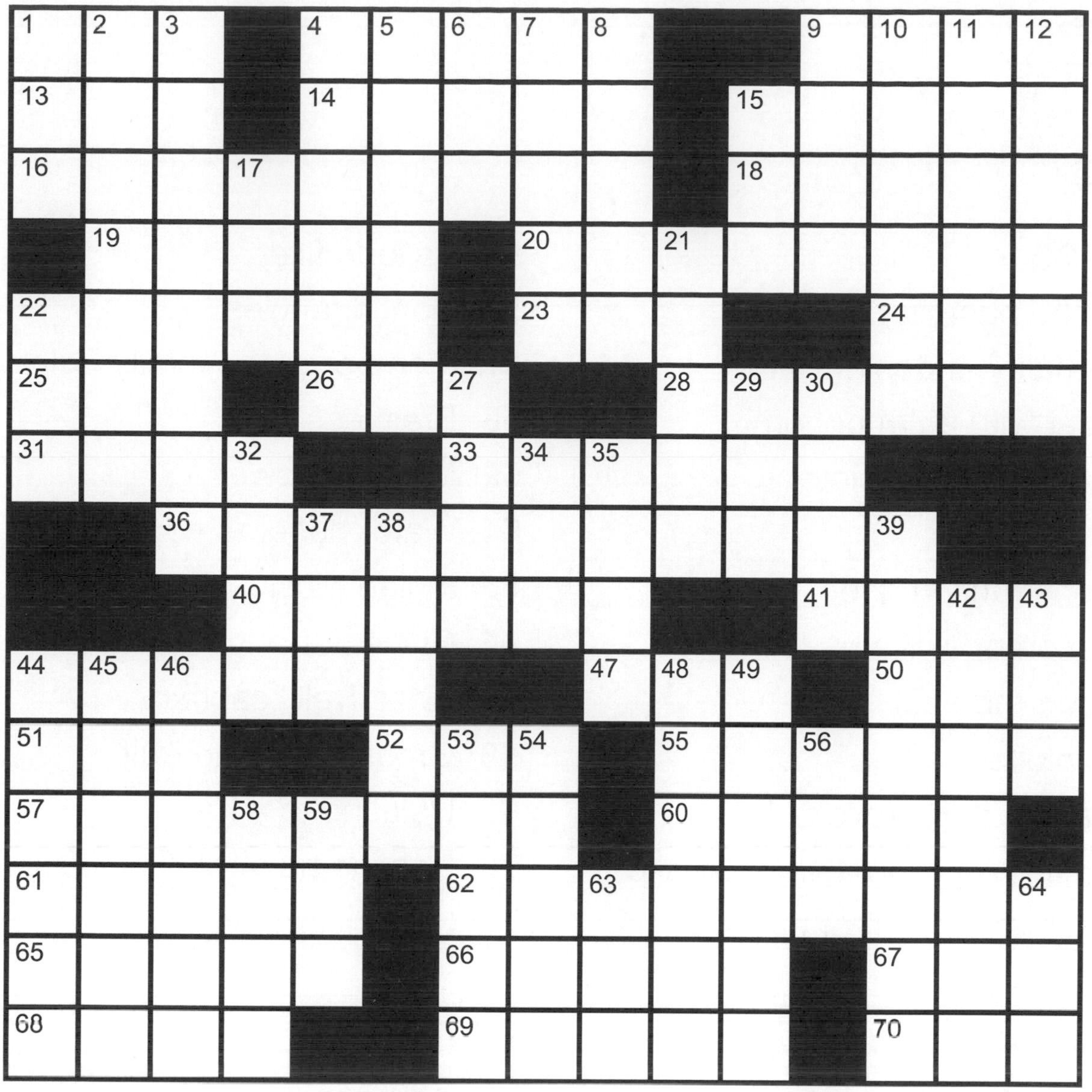

27 Scattered

29 Beer's heavier relative

30 Backwoods affirmative: 2 wds.

32 W.W. II weapon

34 52, in old Rome

35 ___ A Sketch (red toy)

37 Combine

38 Take in again

39 Close-fitting hat

42 Rafters

43 Refrigerator letters, sometimes

44 High standards

45 ___ Trilling, literary critic (1905–75)

46 Imply, with "to"

48 Arousing

49 Red wine

53 Buffalo hockey player

54 Complain

56 Motorist's org.

58 Doodle

59 "___ Rosenkavalier"

63 ___ Mae Brown (Whoopi Goldberg's "Ghost" role)

64 Big inits. at Indy

47

ACROSS

1 In the past, in the past
5 E-mail you don't want
9 Boat with a flat bottom
14 Song for one voice
15 Peewee
16 Construction girder: hyph.
17 Simon or Williams
18 Food morsels
19 Exploits
20 Unable to be revoked
23 Ending for mountain or musket
24 "Master Melvin" of baseball
25 "___ Maria"
26 Cookbook abbr.
29 Wood nymph
31 Big name in stationery
33 Former airline letters
34 "___ So Shy" (Pointer Sisters hit)
36 License giver, initially
37 Talk impulsively
38 Full equipped with weapons: 4 wds.
43 Limerick, e.g.
44 Night before
45 Make a fine design
46 Clinton or Obama, once: abbr.
47 Kind of whale
49 Indian yogurt dish
53 Double curve in a road
54 Balloon filler
55 Contingencies
57 Member of the family Felidae
58 Brainless
62 March follower
64 Water buffalo's cousin
65 Indian music
66 Circle, for one
67 "Star Trek" captain
68 Gross-sounding fruit
69 Relating to a hair
70 Boating hazard
71 "___ here long?"

DOWN

1 Saw
2 Noisy reveler
3 Thin liquid waste
4 Enameled or lacquered metalware
5 Young salmon
6 Buccaneer
7 Against: pref.
8 Failure to correspond
9 Famous London bell: 2 wds.
10 Brutalized Biblical brother
11 Move
12 Channel through sandbanks
13 Dash lengths
21 Put into cipher

1	2	3	4	■	5	6	7	8	■	9	10	11	12	13
14				■	15				■	16				
17				■	18				■	19				
20				21					22				■	■
23			■	24			■	25			■	26	27	28
29			30		■	31	32				■	33		
■	■	■	34		35	■	36			■	37			
38	39	40				41				42				
43				■	44			■	45			■	■	■
46			■	47				48	■	49		50	51	52
53			■	54			■	55	56		■	57		
■	■	58	59				60				61			
62	63				■	64				■	65			
66					■	67				■	68			
69					■	70				■	71			

22 Long-legged bird
27 Kind of team
28 Way to go
30 Interrupter's interjection
32 In pursuit of
35 Deputize: 2 wds.
37 Alpha's follow-up
38 ___ line (major axis of an elliptical orbit)
39 Lobster and beluga products
40 Having notes of fixed rhythmic value (music)
41 Become more successful than
42 Ankles
47 Fast-pitched baseball
48 Nobleman's address
50 When mastodons roamed: 2 wds.
51 Long hair problem
52 Reach
56 Like some pastry
59 Mangrove swamp palm
60 "Idylls of the King" character
61 Eats, slangily
62 Cleopatra biter
63 21st Greek letter

48

ACROSS

1 Some mites
6 A bit loopy
10 Expensively furnished
14 Further down
15 Genesis man
16 Earthen pot
17 Crossing that uses an underpass: 2 wds.
20 "Abdul Abulbul ___" (nonsense song)
21 Lady's title
22 Plague swellings
23 Gravestone, perhaps
25 Yell on a golf course
26 Portable two-way radio: hyph.
32 100 lbs.
35 Locations
36 Advance
37 "Aquarius" musical
39 "Spare" body part
40 Abominable Snowman
41 Eye amorously
42 Breakfast choice
45 Auction offering
46 Dish of melted and seasoned cheese on toast: 2 wds.
49 Paw parts
50 Conquers
53 Shoe cushion
56 Born
58 Kachina doll maker
60 Captions that run the width of a newspaper page: 2 wds.
63 Egyptian goddess
64 Swag
65 Heart or liver
66 Content fully
67 Aching feelings
68 Begin

DOWN

1 Pond dweller
2 Bulblike bases of plants
3 Expect eagerly
4 Sketched afresh
5 Dublin loc.
6 Animal often hit by cars
7 Dangerous biters
8 Airline-regulating org.
9 Large flatfishes
10 Paunch, slangily: hyph.
11 A little of this and a little of that dish
12 Blue-black plumlike fruit
13 ___ Christian Andersen
18 Microscopic
19 A movie star may carry one
24 Baby's seat
25 Hardly hardy

27 Fates, destinies
28 Less emotional
29 "Dallas" actor Howard
30 Crazy about
31 Do some cutting, maybe
32 Dog with a blue-black tongue
33 Worker's reward
34 Money drawer
38 Answer
42 Neat
43 Subsided
44 Classic Christmas gift for dad
47 Fit
48 Casual thing to wear with jeans: hyph.
51 Country, capital Nuku-alofa
52 Asparagus unit
53 Bird venerated by ancient Egyptians
54 Columbia org.
55 Agitated state
56 Brightly colored
57 Devours
59 "___ that funny?"
61 Cake or down preceder
62 "___ Olvidados" (1950 Luis Buñuel film)

49

ACROSS

1 Beatle McCartney
5 Bygone royal
9 Aggregate
14 Directness
16 Hairy-chested
17 Set free
18 Former prisoner: hyph.
19 Bobby of hockey fame
20 Fat letters
21 Did a marathon
23 Peppy piano piece
24 Ivan and Nicholas
26 London and Paris, for example
28 Willow
31 Archaic verb ending
32 Small building: hyph.
36 Rumormonger
40 Cleveland's state
41 Curl one's lip
43 Quick, unexpected attack
44 Drops off
46 Decreased in intensity
48 "Am ___ blame?": 2 wds.
50 Grassy plain
51 Attractive companion accompanying a celebrity: 2 wds.
55 Have for sale
59 Grazing area
60 Eggs on a sushi menu
61 Halloween flyer
63 Courtroom affirmation: 2 wds.
64 Not fulfilled
66 Put down (a full account) in words: 2 wds.
69 Bar code's place
70 Irritation
71 Cut-off from everyone else
72 Farrier's tool
73 Sandwich choices

DOWN

1 Aircraft controller
2 Muslim princes
3 Region of complete shadow
4 "Crouching Tiger, Hidden Dragon" director
5 "The King and I" locale
6 Bald spot hiders
7 Dogfight participant
8 Monster killed by Hercules
9 Comfort
10 Highest amount possible, for short
11 Capital of Ghana
12 Sand bar
13 Musical compositions with words
15 Like upscale parties
22 ___ hangers (motorcycle handlebars)
25 Non-thinking
26 Fiercely, ferociously
27 From that circumstance or source

1	2	3	4	■	5	6	7	8	■	9	10	11	12	13
14				15					■	16				
17									■	18				
19			■	20			■	21	22		■	23		
24			25		■	■	26				27			
■	■	■	28		29	30		■	31			■	■	■
32	33	34						35	■	36		37	38	39
40				■	41				42	■	43			
44				45	■	46				47				
■	■	■	48		49	■	50					■	■	■
51	52	53				54		■	■	55		56	57	58
59			■	60			■	61	62		■	63		
64			65		■	66	67				68			
69					■	70								
71					■	72				■	73			

29 Possibilities
30 Donkey's years
32 Actor Arnold
33 What person?
34 Bike chain application
35 Honest-to-goodness
37 Bert Bobbsey's sister
38 Dead heat
39 Do sums
42 Co. whose mascot is Nipper
45 Catch off guard
47 Full of entanglements
49 "Walking on Thin Ice" singer Yoko
51 "Be-Bop-___" (1956 Gene Vincent hit): hyph.
52 Kidney-related
53 Cuban dance
54 Big name in Scotch whisky
56 Like a fish
57 Draw out
58 Stout twists of fiber
61 Rubbish containers
62 On the peak of
65 Velvet add-on
67 Biology letters
68 Attention, metaphorically

50

ACROSS

1 Hinged door fasteners
6 Forearm bones
11 Garfield or Buchanan: abbr.
14 Everyday
15 Owe ___ of gratitude: 2 wds.
16 Man-mouse connection: 2 wds.
17 "The ___" 2012 sci-fi movie directed by Gary Ross: 2 wds.
19 ___ polloi
20 Farm mother
21 Run into trouble: 3 wds.
23 Make a design, as on a coin
26 Gumbo thickener
27 Evidence that is incontrovertible: 2 wds.
32 Augustan historian
33 Turner and others
34 A.E.C. successor
37 Clandestine maritime org.
38 Person who entices others into wrongdoing
40 Cultural org.
41 Taoism founder Lao-___
42 Spenser's isle
43 "I Ought to ___ Pictures" Neil Simon comedy drama: 2 wds.
44 Completely unaffected by alcohol: 4 wds.
48 Comic Lew
50 "Brideshead Revisited" author, ___ Waugh
51 Ladle: 2 wds.
56 ___ King, bearded giant or goblin of German myth
57 Aviation prefix
58 1992 movie starring Tom Cruise: 4 wds.
63 ___ Offensive
64 Check endorser
65 Slogan
66 Leaky radiator's sound
67 Shooter Adams
68 "Holy moly!"

DOWN

1 "What did you say?"
2 Tempe inst.
3 Closest star to Earth
4 Regal attendant
5 Large number, after "a": 2 wds.
6 Scott Joplin music
7 First wife of Lamech
8 Actress Moore
9 Cynic's snort: 2 wds.
10 "___ raid!": 2 wds.
11 35th President
12 Like Niagara Falls
13 Central Asian gazelle
18 Defendant, at times: abbr.
22 Part of USSR, briefly
23 Actresses Gray and Moran
24 Brief clips at a theater: 2 wds.

1	2	3	4	5	■	6	7	8	9	10	■	11	12	13
14					■	15					■	16		
17					18						■	19		
■	■	■	20			■	21				22			
■	23	24				25	■	■	■	■	26			
27							28	29	30	31			■	■
32				■	■	33					■	34	35	36
37			■	38	39						■	40		
41			■	42					■	■	43			
■	■	44	45						46	47				
48	49			■	■	■	■	50						■
51				52	53	54	55	■	56			■	■	■
57			■	58				59				60	61	62
63			■	64					■	65				
66			■	67					■	68				

25 Fuse two pieces of metal
27 Conspiracy
28 Finnish steam room
29 Should it happen that: 2 wds.
30 ___ Bo (Billy Blanks program)
31 Leb. neighbor
35 Despot's duration
36 Bat Masterson's weapon
38 Bro or sis
39 Before, in poetry
43 Canine symbol of Britain
45 "___ y Plata" (Montana's motto)
46 Chevy model
47 "Smoke Gets in Your Eyes" composer Kern
48 Exams for future attys.
49 Fencing needs
52 California valley known for its wineries
53 End ___ era: 2 wds.
54 180s
55 Affectedly dainty or refined
59 Alternative to shaving cream
60 Kingston Trio hit of 1959
61 Runway guess, for short
62 Discouraging words

51

ACROSS

1 Home
8 Summer Games org.
11 Big race sponsor, initially
14 Loner
15 Flip
17 "Mary Poppins" tune, with "A": 3 wds.
19 "___ who?"
20 Major British tabloid, with "The"
21 Memorable Indian
22 California's Santa ___ Valley
24 Compassionate letters
25 Drop down?
26 Green land
28 Arrow partner
29 56, in old Rome
32 Beyond expectation: 2 wds.
35 "My Name Is Asher ___" (Chaim Potok novel)
36 Common Market inits., once
37 "___ moment"
38 Small stream
41 FAA and IATA code for John Wayne Airport
42 Club headed by the Bakkers, initially
43 Bar order
44 Uses, like a chair: 2 wds.
46 "And this pertains to me … how?"
47 Dental org.
48 Actor Cronyn
49 Ripken, Jr. and Sr.
51 ___ talk (encouraging words)
52 Johns, for short
56 ___ ware (Japanese porcelain)
58 Farm female
59 Big load
60 Be a role model, e.g.: 4 wds.
65 CIA head John
66 Chest protector
67 Console for playing Super Mario Bros., initially
68 "No more seats," briefly
69 Spanish mackerels

DOWN

1 In a snit
2 Colorado resort
3 Hard stuff
4 U.N. arm
5 "Baywatch" complexion
6 Law enforcement and tax collection agency, initially
7 Make disheveled
8 Apple glyph
9 Big galoot
10 "Strangers and Brothers" author: 2 wds.
11 Unable to see
12 Russian ruler: var.
13 Andean nation
16 Gibberish-talking "SNL" character ___ Forrester
18 Director Jean-___ Godard
23 #26 of 26

24 Triumvirates
25 Gets to a higher position: 2 wds.
27 Tel Aviv's country: abbr.
28 ___ canto (singing style)
30 "___, vidi, vici"
31 Words of confidence: 2 wds.
32 Deals with a spill, perhaps
33 Not fooled by
34 Moves to a new place
35 Car nut
39 Churchill's sign
40 "Ed Wood" director Burton
45 Abbr. to the left of a number
47 Coordinates
48 Lumberjacks
50 Flaherty's "Man of ___"
51 Green bean, for example
53 Brokerage phrase: 2 wds.
54 Europe's longest river
55 Dirks of yore
56 Library cataloging datum, briefly
57 Mother of France
58 "Dove ___" (Mozart aria)
61 Ben-Hur was chained to one
62 12, to a Roman
63 First name at Gettysburg
64 Computer program instruction: abbr.

52

ACROSS

1 Ballet move
5 Even, as a score
9 Poker announcement: 2 wds.
14 "If all ___ fails…"
15 Delhi princess
16 Call
17 Certain Muslim dancer: 2 wds.
20 Like some Internet connections: hyph.
21 Orchestra: abbr.
22 Fall times: abbr.
23 ___ out (just managed)
25 North African ruler
27 "Casablanca" pianist
30 Noble, in Essen
32 "Ugly Betty" role
36 Dies ___
38 Opposite of "sans"
40 Have ___ (drink ale): 2 wds.
41 Bakery offering: 2 wds.
44 Small racers
45 ___ Fein
46 "The Time Machine" race
47 Good-for-nothing
49 Aircraft accident investigators, initially
51 Close down
52 "___ Lisa"
54 ___ the finish: 2 wds.
56 Prefix with sphere
59 Actor Gulager
61 Skilled opinion
65 Creamy, spongy desserts: 2 wds.
68 Fleshy fruit with a stone
69 ___ bit (slightly): 2 wds.
70 Early baseball Hall-of-Famer ___ Rixey
71 Easy or secure
72 Bounders down under
73 Sailing ropes

DOWN

1 Bawdy
2 Like some textbook publishers: hyph.
3 Himalayas' home
4 Hostess Mesta
5 Having three feet
6 "At Seventeen" singer Janis
7 Some M.I.T. grads
8 "___ ever wonder…": 2 wds.
9 Flawed somehow: abbr.
10 Likely to bring good luck
11 Lyrical
12 It's just one thing after another
13 Homer Simpson exclamations
18 Gospel writer
19 "Harry Potter" actress Watson
24 Gods in Vedic mythology

26 Innovative Apple computer
27 Crazy person, slangily
28 Buddhist who has attained Nirvana
29 New Zealand native
31 Accept: 2 wds.
33 Author Zora ___ Hurston
34 "Prime Time" footballer Sanders
35 Ban alternative
37 One with a slight build
39 Prefix with grade
42 ___ buco (Italian dish)
43 Catches
48 An old Exxon name
50 "On & On" singer Erykah
53 Aisle stop
55 Image maker: 2 wds.
56 Band with the 2008 album "Black Ice"
57 Drive-___
58 Art Spiegelman's comic rodent
60 1960s spy plane: 2 wds.
62 Early Bill Cosby show: 2 wds.
63 French chef's mushroom
64 Those girls, to Juanita
66 "Law," in Spanish
67 Want ad initials

53

ACROSS

1 Ad ___ per aspera (Kansas' motto)
6 ___-Anne-de-Beaupré
9 Discharged
14 "But you told me that..." retort: 2 wds.
15 French marshal in the Napoleonic Wars (1769–1815)
16 "___ Time": Hemingway stories: 2 wds.
17 Deserved
18 Under-the-sink items
20 Overseas bank service: 2 wds.
22 Daughter of Theia
23 Canadian province: abbr.
24 "Arabian Nights" name
27 8½" x 11" paper size: abbr.
30 Letters on a rubber check
32 Spanish queens
35 Calif. neighbor
37 Of superficial relevance
40 Kitchen device
42 "Chunk" preceder
43 "___ Mio": 2 wds.
44 Guard
47 Art sch. class
48 Globe position?
49 Catch a glimpse of
51 Carrier to Stockholm, for short
52 Dover's state: abbr.
53 551 on a monument
56 Section of I-278, initially
58 Foodstuff also known as sanguinaccio or boudin noir: 2 wds.
64 "We've already covered this ...": 3 wds.
67 Carpet fiber
68 "If ___" (Beatles song): 2 wds.
69 1988 Dennis Quaid remake
70 Microwave feature
71 "That time of year thou ___ in me behold" (Shakespeare's Sonnet 73)
72 Shares of a corp.
73 Like some questions: 2 wds.

DOWN

1 Arrogance, so to speak
2 Burger topping
3 South American monkey
4 "Touched by an Angel" co-star
5 Appends: 2 wds.
6 1960s civil rights org.
7 Phone service
8 Keep an ___ (watch closely): 2 wds.
9 Certain Scandinavian
10 J. Smithson founded one, briefly
11 Lobster spawn
12 Pol., Port., etc.
13 Hospital V.I.P.s
19 Other: Fr.
21 ___ prof.
24 Negative particles
25 Second smallest Teletubby: hyph.
26 Specks in the sea

1	2	3	4	5	■	6	7	8	■	9	10	11	12	13
14					■	15			■	16				
17					■	18			19					
20					21							■	■	■
■	■	■	22			■	23			■	■	24	25	26
27	28	29	■	30		31	■	■	32	33	34			
35			36	■	37		38	39						
40				41	■	42			■	43				
44					45				46	■	47			
48						■	■	49		50	■	51		
52			■	■	53	54	55	■	56		57	■	■	■
■	■	■	58	59				60				61	62	63
64	65	66							■	67				
68					■	69			■	70				
71					■	72			■	73				

27 Held (over someone's head)
28 Three-element vacuum tube
29 Draw back in horror
31 Imposter
33 "Another Green World" composer
34 "___ Gift" (W. C. Fields movie): 2 wds.
36 Frobe who played Goldfinger
38 Fiber knot
39 Some college tests, for short
41 "Citizen Kane" studio, briefly
45 Hungarian mathematician Paul
46 Country music's McEntire
50 Fairness
54 Piles on
55 Blockhead
57 "Ah, Wilderness!" mother
58 Units of sound
59 Cheerful tune
60 Badlands Natl. Park locale: 2 wds.
61 24-hr. conveniences
62 "By the Time I Get to Phoenix" singer Campbell
63 One Saarinen
64 Calculus calculation: abbr.
65 "___ tree falls in the forest…": 2 wds.
66 "The Star-Spangled Banner" composer

54

ACROSS

1 Vinegar, for one
5 Bed support
9 Directly
14 Chat: hyph.
16 Fragrant rootstock used in perfumes
17 "No Mother to Guide Her" novelist: 2 wds.
18 ___ way out (finds a solution): 2 wds.
19 Brit. news network
20 Dearie
21 Menlo Park monogram
23 Early role-playing game co., initially
24 Windblown silt
26 Receptacles for cigarette ends
28 Obviously enjoy, as humor: 2 wds.
31 Resident's suffix
32 Began to deal with (with "on"): 2 wds.
35 Former Defense Secretary Les
39 "God Help the Child" author Morrison
40 Houses, in Spain
42 Besides
43 Group of eight
45 Computer program that's free for a while
47 Birthplace of Constantine the Great
49 With hopes of being sold: 2 wds.
50 Place of fabulous wealth: 2 wds.
54 Notions
57 Gamboling spot
58 Come ___ standstill: 2 wds.
59 Series finale
61 Computer monitor, for short
62 Object of an old French cheer: 2 wds.
64 Reached maturity: 3 wds.
67 She "Doesn't Live Here Anymore"
68 Tangled shrubs and thorny bushes
69 ___ of time
70 "The law is ___..." (Dickens): 2 wds.
71 Doing nothing

DOWN

1 What a dog or cat usually has: 2 wds.
2 100, in Naples
3 Traveling from place to place
4 Sleuth: abbr.
5 W.W. II battle town: 2 wds.
6 Boxer Spinks
7 From ___ Z: 2 wds.
8 Exams
9 Stone name
10 Boiling blood
11 "On the Record" host Van Susteren
12 Sounding like a snake
13 Peter and others
15 Sounds some approval from a distance: 2 wds.
22 Hawaii tuna
25 2004 All-Star Game MVP Alfonso
26 Sneeze sound

27 Mended
29 Word before room or center: abbr.
30 Rehan, Lovelace and others
32 Pou ___, standing place
33 It has a lot of chapters, initially
34 It may be eaten with chicken tikka masala
36 Item seen at a banquet: 2 wds.
37 UN member since 1949: abbr.
38 Formerly known as
41 Some name suffixes
44 Contaminates
46 Animals that live on the surface of another
48 ___ Tomé and Principe (African republic)
50 Fitzgerald and others
51 “Futurama” character with purple hair
52 “Splish Splash” singer Bobby
53 Bangladesh’s capital, old-style
55 Wild sheep of Asia
56 Commemorative marker
59 Dec. holiday
60 Casual agreements
63 Need to tidy things away all the time, say: inits.
65 “It just came to me!”
66 Thurs. follower

55

ACROSS

1 Cease
5 "Eso ___" (Paul Anka hit)
9 Afternoon: Sp.
14 Pressure unit
15 Eastern pooh-bah
16 Suffered a financial loss, slangily: 2 wds.
17 Bob Hoskins's role in "Hook"
18 Bela Lugosi's "Son of Frankenstein" role
19 Arguments
20 Explode in anger: 3 wds.
23 Clinton Cabinet member
24 Simmons sister company
25 Bridal ring: 2 wds.
30 Equally hard to locate: 2 wds.
31 Assents
32 "Deadwood" figure
36 Fox, e.g.
37 Snapshot, for short
38 World-weariness
39 Suffix for man, ten or pen
40 Antioxidant additive, initially
41 Record holders?: hyph.
42 Attracted a lot of attention: 3 wds.
44 Back, in a way
47 "Me as well": 2 wds.
48 Betrays: hyph.
53 Renaissance fiddle
54 Invent, as a new word
55 Commando weapons
57 "___ Man", John Ciardi poem: 3 wds.
58 E. ___ (hazard to health)
59 Change
60 Round dance
61 Irish New Age artist
62 ___ out a draw (narrowly avoids defeat, in chess)

DOWN

1 Ave. intersectors
2 ___ of the Unknowns
3 Baseball great Hershiser
4 Doom
5 New Jersey City across from Staten Island
6 Christmas drink
7 Brogan or pump
8 Rower's pair
9 Sampled
10 How some stocks are sold: 2 wds.
11 Strike back
12 Chicago Bears coaching legend Mike
13 Alien life forms, for short
21 Eccentric
22 Nine-digit IDs
25 G.I. Janes

1	2	3	4		5	6	7	8		9	10	11	12	13
14					15					16				
17					18					19				
	20			21					22					
			23						24					
25	26	27					28	29						
30							31				32	33	34	35
36						37				38				
39					40				41					
				42				43						
	44	45	46					47						
	48					49	50					51	52	
53						54					55			56
57						58					59			
60						61					62			

26 Actor Morales of “NYPD Blue”

27 Bond classic: 2 wds.

28 Nightclub (Fr.)

29 Org. that offers the Canine Good Citizen program

32 Item put in the same envelope as a letter

33 Indonesian buffalo

34 Takes part in a race

35 Word of contempt

37 Prof.’s degree, maybe

38 Montreal team

40 Blubber

41 European country, capital Tallinn

42 Woman’s hat, once

43 In a jaunty manner

44 Swelling

45 Dynamite inventor

46 As a result of: 2 wds.

49 Brutus’s “Behold!”

50 Animal whose fur was used for Crockett’s cap

51 Book before Daniel: abbr.

52 ___ dish (not the main course)

53 Fix

56 “Mayday!”

56

ACROSS

1 ___-di-dah
4 Sunblock ingredient, initially
8 Milk dispenser
13 "A Theory of Semiotics" author
14 Black quartz
15 Carolers' songs
16 "Gone With the Wind" plantation
18 When doubled, a food fish
19 Luau dances
20 Bears: Lat.
21 George Orwell's alma mater
22 Parting words, briefly
23 Lorry fill-up
25 "Darby ___ and the Little People" (1959 Disney film)
27 Disguise
29 Words to a ship's captain: 2 wds.
33 PASCAL predecessor
36 Come ___ end: 2 wds.
38 "Nothin' ___ Good Time" (1988 hit): 2 wds.
39 Fate
40 Bygone MTV show
41 Hay amounts
42 Mosque V.I.P.
43 Japanese noodles
44 Appropriate
45 Bigwigs
47 Is sure to be heard
49 1933 physics Nobelist Paul
51 Submerged threats of W.W. II: hyph.
55 Cars
58 Short and sweet review?
60 "Typee" sequel
61 Golden, in Granada: 2 wds.
62 E. ___, bacteria
63 Astronaut Armstrong
64 "Manhattan Murder Mystery" director
65 Christmas gifts, often
66 Hearst kidnap grp.
67 "Hop on Pop" author
68 Trick-taking game
69 Homily: abbr.

DOWN

1 Abate: 2 wds.
2 Without ___ in the world: 2 wds.
3 Earth's crust
4 Big citrus fruit
5 Med school subj.
6 Somehow: 5 wds.
7 Firing
8 Wicked
9 Musical instrument: 2 wds.
10 Kind of sandwich
11 Israeli oil port: var.
12 Letters for distributing news to Web users
17 Certain officers in the Brit. mil.: 2 wds.

1	2	3	■	■	4	5	6	7	■	8	9	10	11	12
13			■	■	14				■	15				
16			17	■	18				■	19				
20				■	21				■	22				
23				24		■	25		26			■	■	■
■	■	■	27			28		■	29			30	31	32
33	34	35			■	36		37		■	38			
39					■	40			■	41				
42				■	43				■	44				
45				46		■	47		48			■	■	■
■	■	■	49			50		■	51			52	53	54
55	56	57			■	58		59		■	60			
61					■	62				■	63			
64					■	65				■	■	66		
67					■	68				■	■	69		

24 Spanish cooking pot
26 “Jurassic Park” mathematician ___ Malcolm
28 Quintillionth: prefix
30 George Takei’s role in “Star Trek”
31 Brain passage
32 File
33 Blood-related
34 Holy man
35 Act greedily, perhaps
37 Wings of an insect
41 Fall planting
43 Kazakhstan letters, once
46 Buffaloes
48 Elizabethan ballad player, perhaps
50 Bank holdings: abbr.
52 Make ___ of: 2 wds.
53 Linen fabric
54 Kind of energy
55 Nabokov heroine and others
56 River through Congo
57 Cough-syrup ingredient
59 ___ Ulyanov, Vladimir Lenin’s father

57

ACROSS

1 Go aboard
7 Bug someone, e.g.
10 Biscuit bits
14 Actress Madison, Harper in "Parental Guidance"
15 Surprised cry
16 Cold cuts, e.g.
17 Corporeal, physical
18 Off-road motorcycle
20 Conical tent: var.
22 Trainee
23 "Mad Men" protagonist Draper
26 Creme de ___
28 Elementary particle
29 Aid in criminal activity
31 Religious doctrine
33 "Star Trek" rank: abbr.
34 Cinema film
36 Tenant farmer
39 Annoying person
41 Imaginary
44 Update (a web page)
46 W.W. I soldier
47 Braying beast
49 Speedy
51 Butcher's offering
52 Action film staple
55 "Taking Terri Mueller" author, Norma Fox ___
57 Holiday drink with nutmeg
58 What a crossword clue might be
60 Blue-pencil
62 Heating appliance
64 African nation once run by Idi Amin
68 A single one
69 Compass dir.
70 Office machine
71 ___ out a living (barely gets by)
72 Encountered
73 Threefold

DOWN

1 Go out, on the beach
2 "The Little Red Book" writer
3 Signal at auction
4 Came down
5 Archeologist's find
6 Calculator feature
7 Lawn layer
8 Speculate or theorize about issues
9 Auld lang syne
10 Card game
11 Act of putting something back into its previous position
12 Tackle (an opponent): 2 wds.
13 Rears
19 Ayr man's hat

1	2	3	4	5	6	■	7	8	9	■	10	11	12	13
14						■	15			■	16			
17						■	18			19				
■	■	■	20			21	■	22						
23	24	25	■	26			27		■	28				
29			30	■	31				32	■	■	33		
34				35	■	36				37	38		■	■
39					40		■	41					42	43
■	■	44					45		■	46				
47	48		■	■	49				50	■	51			
52			53	54	■	55				56	■	57		
58					59		■	60			61	■	■	■
62							63	■	64			65	66	67
68				■	69			■	70					
71				■	72			■	73					

21 Scoop holder: 3 wds.
23 Censure
24 "O" in old radio lingo
25 Refuse to give in: 3 wds.
27 It goes in your lungs
30 Ocean motion
32 Speedometer letters
35 One of Santa's Little Helpers
37 Father, to Huck Finn
38 Chemical compound suffix
40 "To ___ is human ..."
42 Assortment
43 ___ bean
45 Watering hole
47 Build up
48 Got smaller
50 Subtract
53 Meat skewers
54 Pilot's announcement, for short
56 Inflexibility
59 Any thing
61 Cassette contents
63 Not working any longer: abbr.
65 Bird's beak
66 ___ Monte (Libby's rival)
67 Lionel Richie's "You ___"

58

ACROSS

1 Lots and lots
6 "Daniel Boone" star Parker
10 Class action grp.
13 Member state of the United Arab Emirates
14 Late English princess
15 Opposite of vert.
16 Have ___ for (be perceptive to): 2 wds.
17 Not here
19 "Born Yesterday" playwright Garson
20 ___ nitrate
21 Intl. feminine group
22 Political cartoonist Thomas
24 Dolt
26 Additions
29 Doofus: var.
31 Destroy and then some
35 1968 Cream hit: 2 wds.
37 Arterial vessel
38 "There's ___ in My Dirt!" (Gary Larson book): 2 wds.
39 Never, in German
40 Seed again
41 ___-frutti
42 Shaking or quivering slightly
44 Roughly-built cabin
45 Tennis star Tommy
46 World's first rocket-powered full-size aircraft
47 Harness part
49 Civil rights org. founded in 1960
51 French river
54 Dark and murky
56 Market online
60 Reacting in an offended or angry way
62 Russian woman's name
63 Huge Brit. lexicon
64 Log-rolling competition
65 Fashionable beach resorts
66 Publishers' hirees, for short
67 Lawsuit beneficiary
68 Part of a movie

DOWN

1 Pierre's state: abbr., 2 wds.
2 Roman moon goddess
3 Black, in poetry
4 Laughed uncontrollably: 3 wds.
5 Tuscan tourist town
6 Thin coating or layer
7 Motto of a big spender, perhaps: 4 wds.
8 Fishhook line
9 Lumberjack's tool
10 Expression of relief or tiredness
11 Ancient neck ornament

12 Acreage

14 Agatha Christie novel: 4 wds.

18 Like some dams

23 Lat. or Lith., once

25 Port town on the coast of the Sea of Japan

26 Belts

27 "Yeah": 2 wds.

28 2003 Mazda roadster

30 "Chaplin" actress Kelly

32 Firestarter's crime

33 Thickset

34 Hole that an anchor rope passes through

36 Actress Alexander of "The Cosby Show"

43 AOL rival

48 "Amadeus" director Forman

50 Tops a room

51 Wind instrument

52 Really steamed

53 Vicious and Caesar

55 Place for a pad, in football

57 White House staffer

58 ___ a secret: 2 wds.

59 Emit a powerful beam

61 Capote, to friends

59

ACROSS

1 "The Family Circus" cartoonist
6 Earth sci.
10 Boom or gaff
14 Young Jetson
15 Biblical brother
16 Uses scissors
17 Please, in Potsdam
18 Mexican entree: 2 wds.
20 Yellowfin tuna
21 Weak one
23 Sheiks' cliques
24 Brown bison
26 Champagne Tony of golf
27 Suffix with cheer or cheek
28 Disease caused by a lack of thiamine
32 Minor Hebrew prophet
34 Calyx component
35 Islet
36 Mine entrance
37 Actress Uta ___
38 Major golf tourneys, initially
39 ___ fault: 2 wds.
40 Guadalajara guy
41 Decoration fixed to the surface of something else
42 Backstreet feline: 2 wds.
44 Aunt Bee's boy, in 1960s TV
45 _____-Seltzer
46 Affixes T-shirt designs: 2 wds.
49 Prayer book
52 Genetic molecules, initially
53 Cost-of-living no.
54 Artificial
56 Future fungus
58 Nile queen, informally
59 Half of an Orkan farewell
60 Bar order, with "the"
61 Locale of William the Conqueror's tomb
62 "The Immoralist" author
63 Fables

DOWN

1 Meal on a skewer
2 ___ Root, Nobelist for Peace: 1912
3 Synthetic
4 Negating word
5 Balderdash
6 Artist's mixture
7 Those, in Toledo
8 Blockhead
9 Certain Protestant
10 Sacred beetle of ancient Egypt
11 Brownish purple
12 Bit of physics
13 Online feeds, initially
19 Dravidian language
22 Last: abbr.
25 Accomplishment

1	2	3	4	5	■	6	7	8	9	■	10	11	12	13
14					■	15				■	16			
17					■	18				19				
20			■	21	22			■	23					
24			25				■	26				■	■	■
■	■	27				■	28					29	30	31
32	33				■	34					■	35		
36				■	37					■	38			
39			■	40					■	41				
42			43					■	44				■	■
■	■	■	45				■	46					47	48
49	50	51				■	52				■	53		
54						55			■	56	57			
58				■	59				■	60				
61				■	62				■	63				

26 Persona non grata
28 Brought forth
29 Jamboree attendee who has earned many merit badges: 2 wds.
30 Fighter of pirates, initially
31 Bitsy beginning
32 ___ Hari
33 False god
34 Capital of Yemen
37 Shouting to interrupt a speech
38 Nabokov book set in upstate New York
40 "Heroes" villain
41 Western Hemisphere marsupial
43 "For Your Eyes Only" singer, 1981
44 Old Danish coin
46 ___ course: 2 wds.
47 Big name in book clubs
48 Nobelist Bohr
49 1300, to Caesar
50 Kansas city on the Neosho River
51 Dagger
52 Divide
55 Rock guitarist Steve
57 "Gangnam Style" rapper

60

ACROSS

1 Cir. midpoint
4 Memory: prefix
8 Fight the powers that be
13 500 sheets
15 College in New Rochelle
16 Egg-shaped
17 Actress Samms
18 Landers and others
19 "___ The Beat" (Go-Go's hit): 2 wds.
20 Commentator at a game
23 Halloween getup
24 Capers
28 Hoppy glassful, for short
29 World created by Jim Henson for the movie "The Dark Crystal"
31 French pronoun
32 "The Astonishing Elephant" author Alexander
35 Leader
36 Suffix with tutor or torrent
37 "Too Weird to Live, Too Rare to Die" band: 4 wds.
41 Continue
42 Cyclops, Storm, Wolverine, et al
43 Leaves out
44 A.A.A. recommendation: abbr.
45 Bothers
46 Cries of sorrow: var.
47 Balkan province
49 Used as a climbing aid: 2 wds.
53 Character in Lewis Carroll's "Through the Looking Glass": hyph.
56 Record material
59 Artist Bonheur
60 Balm for a burn
61 Awards for dramas, familiarly
62 "___ pronounce you man and wife": 2 wds.
63 Tune for two
64 Small woods
65 Cable offering, initially
66 Barbecue sound

DOWN

1 Dimin.'s musical opposite
2 Beat
3 12th president of the Philippines
4 Unpleasant atmosphere
5 Present occasion
6 Sicilian city
7 Catholic service
8 Ivanhoe's love
9 Six-time U.S. Open tennis champ
10 Breathalyzer attachment
11 1944 initials
12 Give the go-ahead
14 Drink with a twist
21 Late name in rap
22 Late, in Spain
25 Grammarian's "Who's there?" reply: 3 wds.

1	2	3	■	■	4	5	6	7	■	8	9	10	11	12
13			14	■	15				■	16				
17				■	18				■	19				
20				21					22			■	■	■
23							■	■	24			25	26	27
■	■	■	28			■	29	30			■	31		
32	33	34			■	35				■	■	36		
37					38					39	40			
41			■	■	42				■	43				
44			■	45				■	46			■	■	■
47			48			■	■	49				50	51	52
■	■	■	53			54	55							
56	57	58			■	59				■	60			
61					■	62				■	63			
64					■	65				■	■	66		

26 Do together
27 Crop containers
29 Heads overseas?
30 1980s scandal figure Jessica
32 Bit of inspiration
33 Couldn't avoid: 2 wds.
34 Chilean range
35 Code in which many Web pages are written, initially
38 "If it ain't broke, don't fix it," e.g.
39 "___ Believe?" 2015 movie starring Mira Sorvino: 2 wds.
40 Outburst from a furious person: 3 wds.
45 Tear away by force
46 Early in the morning: 2 wds.
48 "But of course!": 2 wds.
49 Online administrator, briefly
50 Grade that's not so good: 2 wds.
51 Siouan tribesmen
52 Russian negatives
54 ___-dieu
55 Heavy weights
56 Singer: abbr.
57 Nigerian native
58 Puppy's bite

61

ACROSS

1 Kind of shoppe
5 Ancient
9 Bingo call: 2 wds.
13 Interchanges
16 Units of sound
17 Shocking
18 Lilith's portrayer on "Cheers"
19 Concert ender, often
20 Comedy show with Candy, Short, Moranis, et al.
22 Tic-___ (metronome sound)
23 Great Salt Lake site
25 Hold in trust
27 Musical set in Argentina
30 Small batteries' letters
32 Excited, with "up"
33 Muscle quality
34 The "I" in T.G.I.F.
35 Fast and lively, in music
38 TV alien who ate cats
39 Pull along heavily: var.
41 ___ an der Thaya, Austrian town
42 Smother
44 Med. feeders
45 Adjusts, as a clock
46 Highest note in Guido's scale
47 Gibbon, for one
48 Topsy-___
49 Union general Henry Warner ___
51 Evening, in France
53 Rx instruction, initially
54 Had memorized
56 Fix
60 Significance
62 "The Misfits" costar: 2 wds.
64 On Sunset Blvd., e.g.: 2 wds.
65 Incidental topics: 2 wds.
66 Gives an opinion
67 Millions of centuries
68 "ER" command

DOWN

1 "Top ___ mornin' to you": 2 wds.
2 Scientologist founder Hubbard: 2 wds.
3 Jeanne ___, French heroine
4 In transit, in France: 2 wds.
5 Sleep disorder
6 Supernatural being
7 Those, to Carlos
8 Low pair
9 Consumer protection org.
10 Person who never drinks alcohol
11 Arm bender
12 Fraction of a min.: 2 wds.
14 Brand in the bedroom
15 Jet set jets, for short
21 TV monitor of sorts: hyph.
24 "What ___ God wrought?"
26 Gun, as the engine
27 Greek letters

1	2	3	4	■	5	6	7	8	■	■	9	10	11	12
13				14					15	■	16			
17										■	18			
19						■	20			21	■	22		
■	■	■	23			24	■	25			26			■
27	28	29			■	30	31		■	32			■	■
33				■	34			■	35				36	37
38			■	39				40			■	41		
42			43			■	44			■	45			
■	■	46			■	47			■	48				
■	49				50		■	51	52			■	■	■
53			■	54			55	■	56			57	58	59
60			61	■	62			63						
64				■	65									
66				■	■	67				■	68			

28 Electric unit

29 Rule in baseball: 2 wds.

31 It was ___ of the tongue: 2 wds.

34 Drink cooler

35 C.E.O.'s subordinates

36 Broadcasting system, initially

37 Like child's play

39 Loose

40 Nights before

43 Waitress at Mel's

45 Outdo

47 ___ Bedelia (children's book character)

48 1970s icon Cheryl ___

49 ___ Heights University, Adrian, Michigan

50 Mom's brothers, briefly

52 Terminix rival

53 The item here

55 Walk in water

57 Border upon

58 Police officer training school in Plainfield, initially

59 Break

61 Professor's helpers, initially

63 Rock's ___ Speedwagon

62

ACROSS

1 Mexican's assent: 2 wds.
5 City west of Daytona Beach
10 "Serpico" author
14 Old French coins
15 Provoking laughter
16 Sans purpose
17 "The ___" 1973 movie that won an Oscar for John Houseman: 2 wds.
19 Cinematographer Nykvist
20 Things to follow: 2 wds.
21 Private pupils
23 Reply to a ques.
24 "Flying" Field role
25 Kind of roll
26 "___ be my pleasure!"
27 Break in the action
28 "Law & Order: ___": inits.
31 Chest muscles, for short
34 Arab chief
36 Diarist Nin
38 Unable to think of a response: 5 wds.
41 Thief, slangily
42 Apollo astronaut Slayton
43 Month before Sivan
44 East, to Germans
45 General ___ Chicken (Chinese menu dish)
47 Nothing
49 Does what one's told
51 Did nothing
52 Bus. school degree
55 Strappy shoe
57 Unyielding
59 ___ butter
60 1984 Prince album: 2 wds.
62 Like a yenta
63 Deride: 2 wds.
64 Are, in Argentina
65 Holy Fr. women
66 Acts as an usher
67 Lawyers: abbr.

DOWN

1 Anatomical dividers
2 Corporate raider Carl
3 Apartment VIPs, for short
4 Elbe feeder
5 Blocks
6 Singer Leonard
7 Latin 101 word
8 Fleur-de-___
9 Colorless ketone
10 Bollito ___ (Italian dish of mixed meats)
11 Mortal enemy
12 Nautical direction
13 Dict. entries
18 Litter castoff, often
22 International jurisprudence: 2 wds.

1	2	3	4	■	5	6	7	8	9	■	10	11	12	13
14				■	15					■	16			
17				18						■	19			
20							■	21	22					
23			■	24		■	25						■	■
■	■	■	26			■	27				■	28	29	30
31	32	33		■	34	35			■	36	37			
38				39					40					
41					■	42				■	43			
44			■	45	46			■	47	48		■	■	■
■	■	49	50				■	51			■	52	53	54
55	56					■	57				58			
59				■	60	61								
62				■	63					■	64			
65				■	66					■	67			

25 Impresario Sol

26 Archipelago part

27 "___ What You Make It" (Hannah Montana song)

29 "Livin' la ___ Loca"

30 Old atlas initials

31 When doubled, the territorial capital of American Samoa

32 Greek vowels that look like an H

33 Chinese dialect

35 Windows precursor: hyph.

37 Shred of waste silk

39 Not one's cup ___: 2 wds.

40 Dauphine and Le Car

46 Graceful girls

48 Beatles' song, "Let___": 2 wds.

50 Times to give gifts, briefly

51 March honoree, familiarly

52 Show off

53 Bond girl Ekland

54 Paquin and Pavlova

55 Phisher's acquisitions, for short

56 Like ___ knife through butter: 2 wds.

57 Sp. girl

58 Town north of Anaheim, California

61 Quick turnaround, slangily

63

ACROSS

1 Assigner of Gs and Rs, initially
5 ___ and seek
9 Contempt
14 Actor Van Dyke
15 Organic compound suffix
16 Flavored like some mouthwash
17 Distinguishing trait
19 Become, eventually: 2 wds.
20 Suffix with adopt or address
21 Suggestions on food labels, initially
22 Leprechaun's land
23 "...and pretty maids all in ___": 2 wds.
24 Faucet for drawing water from a pipe
27 Former film critic Janet
30 Made progress: 2 wds.
31 "Peer Gynt Suite" composer
32 Hawaiian hello
33 Special effects letters
36 Faulty reckonings
39 Thing settled in a bar
40 Little laugh: hyph.
41 Every 60 minutes
42 Unfolded
44 Checks the growth of
45 Followers of a Chinese philosophy
47 High spots
48 Wile E. Coyote's favorite company
49 Italian city with a leaning tower
50 Retail estab.
53 Rum and lime drink, Cuba ___
55 Punster's word
57 "___ you!" (challenger's cry): 2 wds.
58 Miss ___ (TV psychic)
59 In the near future
60 Pale-looking
61 "___ Hers" Pulp album of 1994
62 College entrance exams, initially

DOWN

1 Store's goods, for short
2 Snowman prop
3 High cards
4 Dog breeder's org.
5 Collision type: 2 wds.
6 Family member, after a wedding: hyph.
7 Studs
8 Seat of White Pine County, Nev.
9 "Take Me Bak ___" (1972 Slade single)
10 Moolah
11 Type of maize used for decoration: 2 wds.
12 Complete reversal: hyph.
13 Term of affection: 2 wds.

1	2	3	4	■	5	6	7	8	■	9	10	11	12	13
14				■	15				■	16				
17				18					■	19				
20			■	21				■	■	■	22			
■	■	■	23				■	24	25	26				
27	28	29				■	30						■	■
31					■	32					■	33	34	35
36					37						38			
39			■	40					■	41				
■	■	42	43					■	44					
45	46						■	47				■	■	■
48				■	■	■	49				■	50	51	52
53				54	■	55					56			
57					■	58				■	59			
60					■	61				■	62			

18 Brings water to

23 “Smart” one

24 Non-native, in Honolulu

25 Jewish youth org.

26 Structure that is very unsafe

27 People in charge: abbr.

28 Diva’s showstopper

29 High school cheer: 2 wds.

30 Provided with a hint

32 Muscle pains

34 Pesky insect

35 Ellis and Long, e.g.: abbr.

37 Period of penitence

38 Promises to pay, initially

43 Capital of South Dakota

44 “Leaving already?”: 2 wds.

45 Shire of “Godfather III”

46 Etching agents

47 Uses a stopwatch

49 ___-sci (coll. major)

50 Marge’s mother-in-law on “The Simpsons”

51 Shoelace problem

52 Addition column

54 Poetic contraction

55 FDR predecessor

56 Owns

64

ACROSS

1 Figure skater Brian
6 Roman goddess of hope
10 Ed.'s request, initially
14 Helpful theorem
15 ___ Bowl
16 Court records
17 Skip ___: 2 wds.
18 Green feeling that's a cardinal sin
19 10th-century pope
20 It's a bore
22 Polite reply from a ranch hand: 2 wds.
24 It may be added to assert or attract
25 Shankar of Indian theater
27 Deliberately avoided
29 Emerald Isle, in verse
33 Chats online with, briefly
34 Plane or level
35 Okla., before 1907
37 Golden Arches sandwich
41 Air letters, once?
42 Built for speed
44 "___ pig's eye!": 2 wds.
45 ___-Davis (Pfizer subsidiary)
48 G.I. awards
49 Promising words
50 Barcelona bear
52 Defeat by more skillful maneuvering
54 Italian dish cooked with broth
58 Benefit
59 1961 Literature Nobelist Andric
60 Add to the staff
62 Turned over and over
66 Pres., militarily: hyph.
68 Alternative to acrylics
70 Dirigible parts
71 Wide widths, initially
72 Mozart's No. 1 through No. 41, briefly
73 "Invisible Cities" writer Calvino
74 Web letters in orange buttons
75 West's bridge partner
76 Annual awards show first hosted by Dennis Miller

DOWN

1 Hydrating cream brand
2 "___: My Story": C&W autobiography
3 Duck variety
4 Common temple name
5 For mature audiences: 2 wds.
6 "___ Bop" (1984 Cyndi Lauper hit)
7 Insignificant
8 Little people
9 Utters "hello": 2 wds.
10 "Dog Day Afternoon" character
11 ___ the hole: 2 wds.
12 Kitchen appliance
13 Like many roofs
21 Goes off on a tirade
23 Champagne producer based in Reims

1	2	3	4	5	■	6	7	8	9	■	10	11	12	13
14					■	15				■	16			
17					■	18				■	19			
20					21	■	22			23	■	24		
■	■	■	25			26	■	27			28			
29	30	31					32	■	33			■	■	■
34				■	35			36	■	37		38	39	40
41			■	■	42				43	■	■	44		
45			46	47	■	48				■	49			
■	■	■	50		51	■	52			53				
54	55	56				57	■	58				■	■	■
59			■	60			61	■	62			63	64	65
66			67	■	68			69	■	70				
71				■	72				■	73				
74				■	75				■	76				

26 Stockbroker's statistic
28 Defense advisory gp.
29 Letters before "://"
30 Hawkeye State
31 Big pig
32 "You ___ Beautiful" (Cocker hit): 2 wds.
36 Romulus's twin brother
38 Gp. against file-sharing
39 Verb type: abbr.
40 Thai money
43 Relatively cool sun: 2 wds.
46 "Kitchy-___!"
47 Book after Neh.
49 Brunch fare
51 Serving no useful purpose
53 Chicago suburb
54 Kitchen aid
55 Clinging plants
56 Loudness units
57 Indian language (relative of Bengali)
61 Some trees
63 Bound
64 Jethro's cousin
65 Brit. decorations
67 Author Lewis et al., initially
69 Boom source, initially

65

ACROSS

1 Remarkable person
5 Frat. letters
9 "Na Laetha Geal M'Óige" singer
13 Popular breakfast restaurant chain
14 Three-time Olympic champion gymnast Aaltonen
15 Bad look
16 Bite
17 NYC diplomat: 2 wds.
18 "House of Frankenstein" director ___ C. Kenton
19 Classic 1930s gangster movie line: 4 wds.
22 Computer file format, initially
23 Put a point on, old-style
24 One who leads a Spartan lifestyle
28 Come up
31 Pier gp.
32 Mother ___ (forty-niner's dream)
35 Circus cries
36 1944 movie directed by Billy Wilder: 2 wds.
41 He played Tony on "NYPD Blue"
42 "Portland, Oregon" singer Loretta
43 Early touring car
44 Passover feast
46 Took on or assumed
49 "The Morning Watch" writer James
51 "Bad" checkup letters
52 1964 Beach Boys hit: 3 wds.
60 Plenty: 2 wds.
61 Eyelid maladies
62 Koh-i- ___ (famed diamond)
63 Prefix meaning 'personal'
64 Coins featuring Pope Benedict XVI
65 Sign of the future
66 Baghdad's ___ City
67 Army mail centers, initially
68 Auction actions

DOWN

1 "The Mod Squad" cop
2 "Looks like trouble!": hyph.
3 Be defeated
4 Musical written by Robert Lopez and Kristen Anderson-Lopez: 2 wds.
5 Hindu princess
6 "B.C." cartoonist
7 British track star Steve
8 Actress Loren
9 Voter's event
10 Roman emperor, AD 54–68
11 Cry out
12 "Iliad" warrior
14 Childish
20 Took a chair
21 Flash memory forerunner, initially
24 Lend a hand

25 Blackthorn fruits

26 Reason

27 Mattress feature

29 Garment for the upper body

30 Cosmetician Lauder

33 Letters after Charles Schumer's name

34 "Giant" author Ferber

37 Ham performer: 2 wds.

38 Feudal lord

39 Infinite

40 Hebrew letter

45 Long arm of the Indian Ocean: 2 wds.

47 Lacking a match

48 Expect to happen: 2 wds.

50 Consume: 2 wds.

52 Speaker's platform

53 Alan of "M*A*S*H"

54 Character to "avoid," in vintage Domino's Pizza ads

55 Laura who wrote "Stoney End"

56 Boardroom V.I.P.s

57 Jack Sheldon song "There's No One Like ___"

58 Kind of college, shortly

59 Coastal raptors

66

ACROSS

1 Artillery burst
6 Contribute
9 Auth. unknown
13 Roswell crash victim, supposedly
14 Mark Harmon series on CBS
15 Director Wertmuller
16 Run away: 2 wds.
18 Newspaper publisher Adolph
19 Ethnic group of Vietnam
20 Kind of battery, initially
21 ___-Hawley Tariff
22 In distinction from others
26 Eastern nurse
29 Got ready
30 Read carefully
33 "Chestnuts roasting ___ open fire…": 2 wds.
34 Intermittently: 4 wds.
40 Ratio phrase: 2 wds.
41 Church counsels
42 Native of Madrid
46 "___ la guerre"
47 Incapable of being reformed
50 Place where milk is kept
51 Fleischer of the West Wing
52 Nigerian native
55 Stu's wife on "Rugrats"
56 Require: 4 wds.
60 General Robt.: 2 wds.
61 Yellow part of an egg
62 Pungent edible bulb
63 Automatic updates from favorite websites, initially
64 "Didn't I tell you?"
65 False: 2 wds.

DOWN

1 Indistinguishable
2 "When I Was ___" ("H.M.S. Pinafore" song): 2 wds.
3 Be fond of
4 Flight formation
5 How some beer is served: 2 wds.
6 Duke's conf.
7 Cartoonist Browne
8 Sheet music markings
9 Puerto Rican baseball players' family name
10 Designer Miller
11 Waiting to be connected: 2 wds.
12 Foul-smelling
14 Civil rights org.
17 "Mask of Death" actress ___ Dawn Chong
21 Meager
22 Feng ___ (art of placement)
23 It's mined in Minnesota's Mesabi Range: 2 wds.
24 Get along
25 Bridge declaration: 2 wds.

26 Set of functions in computing, initially

27 Grown-up boys

28 Dog's bark, in the comics

31 Ungenerous with money

32 Davis of "The Matrix Reloaded"

35 ___ end (over): 2 wds.

36 Suffix for assist or resist

37 Beluga delicacy

38 N.F.L. scores

39 Mach 1 breaker, initially

42 Slow-moving mollusks

43 Groups of lions

44 Lofty perches

45 Took in liquid

47 Milk source

48 "Prince Valiant" character

49 Attach with string: 2 wds.

52 Horizontal passage into a mine

53 Outback critters

54 "River ___ Return" movie starring Mitchum and Monroe: 2 wds.

56 Drive-___ (quick touring visits)

57 Help wanted ad letters

58 ___ d'Orléans

59 North Carolina's ___ River State Park

67

ACROSS

1 Extensive
5 Soviet prison system
10 Censorship-fighting org.
14 Famous shortstop's nickname: hyph.
15 Speed skater ___ Anton Ohno
16 Bearing
17 Perez or Gwynn
18 Protector in the ring
20 Italian article
21 Mark of perfection
22 Some signed notes, initially
23 Electrician, at times
26 "Sorry, you're not ___" (classic rejection): 2 wds.
30 Pointing finger, usually
31 Fits of anger
33 Ending for second or sediment
34 Island country, capital Manama
37 Tennis champ Nastase
38 Hoffman movie of 1982
41 Like beatniks, often
43 Roadie's equipment: abbr.
44 Certain haircuts
46 Direction opposite SSW
47 House in Honduras
48 Architect Jones
52 Interpreter of Judaic law
54 Place to listen to music and enjoy a cocktail: 2 wds.
57 Antioxidant-rich berry
59 Girl of the house: abbr.
60 Approx.
61 Protector on the rink: 2 wds.
65 French weapon
66 Emerald City's creator
67 Up ___ (trapped): 2 wds.
68 Corner-to-corner: abbr.
69 Heraldic border
70 Away: 2 wds.
71 Annapolis inits.

DOWN

1 African tribe that's also a dance
2 Like some patches: hyph.
3 Cartoon duck
4 Dreyer's partner in ice cream
5 Player
6 Barely ahead: 2 wds.
7 Comic Costello
8 Prefix with meter
9 "Can we ___?" (bored child's plea): 3 wds.
10 Not to be missed: 2 wds.
11 Bush Sr. once headed it
12 Celtic sea god
13 "And", to Otto
19 Chaps
21 Greg Abbott's state
24 Money owed
25 Creek
27 Connecticut university

1	2	3	4		5	6	7	8	9		10	11	12	13
14					15						16			
17					18					19				
20				21				22						
23			24				25		26			27	28	29
30							31	32				33		
			34		35	36					37			
38	39	40						41		42				
43					44		45							
46				47						48		49	50	51
52			53				54	55	56					
			57			58		59				60		
61	62	63					64				65			
66					67						68			
69					70						71			

28 ___ blanc (Italian wine grape variety)

29 Got a good look at

32 Capital of Latvia

35 Breed of Persian cat

36 Antique autos, initially

37 "___ Game" David Bowie song: 2 wds.

38 Trig. function

39 Former Atlanta arena

40 German automaker

42 Claude who starred in TV's "Lobo"

45 Fortune

47 Peniston of R&B

49 Genus that comprises the candytufts

50 Certain meter reader

51 Brand of Mexican food

53 Opera by Delibes

55 Japanese immigrant

56 Clay of "American Idol" fame

58 "___ Blame", Kip Moore song of 2015: 2 wds.

61 Cable channel, initially

62 Boat propeller

63 ___-de-sac

64 It may be framed

65 Soccer's Freddy or Fro

68

ACROSS

1 Percussion disks
6 Forbidden: var.
10 Healing sign
14 Tapering to a point
15 Archeological site
16 Bit of water growth
17 Fable writer
18 Sculpting, painting, et al.
19 Hawaiian necklaces
20 Security guard during the hours of darkness: 2 wds.
23 Black gold
24 Parade stopper
25 Gas pump word
29 Soap ingredients
31 Small pouch
34 Cable TV offering: hyph.
36 Fast motion on film
37 Worn out
38 More or less: abbr.
39 Place to see some works by El Greco
40 Ages
41 Penicillin, e.g.
43 Crime family head
44 Common conjunctions
45 Atlas features
46 Fleet
48 Econ. indicator
49 Old machine for showing movies
55 Centers of activity
56 ___ surgeon
57 Arctic abode
59 Big test
60 Jazz bit
61 Sap
62 Cabbagelike veggie
63 Diner sign
64 Glacial deposits

DOWN

1 Govt. property overseer
2 Dentist's directive
3 "Nil ___ bonum"
4 Hot rum drink
5 Removed by suction
6 Dragged fishing net
7 A saint or star may have one
8 Deck post for cables
9 Remove by twisting
10 Ragout of game in a rich sauce
11 New beginning: 2 wds.
12 "Ah'm ___ it!"
13 Undergrad degrees, initially
21 Amphitheater level
22 "Rumor ___ it..."

1	2	3	4	5	■	6	7	8	9	■	10	11	12	13
14					■	15				■	16			
17					■	18				■	19			
■	20				21					22				■
■	■	■	■	23			■	■	24				■	■
25	26	27	28			■	29	30			■	31	32	33
34						35				■	36			
37					■	38			■	39				
40				■	41				42					
43			■	44				■	45					
■	■	46	47			■	■	48			■	■	■	■
■	49					50	51				52	53	54	■
55				■	56				■	57				58
59				■	60				■	61				
62				■	63				■	64				

25 ___ out (declined)
26 Egypt's capital
27 Despotic
28 "Planet of the ___"
29 Catalogs
30 Bhutan beast
32 Tax evader's worry
33 Comfy shoes
35 Peddle
36 Family business abbr.
39 Insignificant wound
41 "Alice doesn't live here ___"
42 Alternative to Google
44 Broadway, e.g.
47 Cartoon art
48 Plays a round
49 Hip joint
50 "E lucevan le stelle," for one
51 27th U.S. president
52 Muslim honorific
53 Purple fruit
54 Computer key
55 Albanian coin
58 Mission control, for short

69

ACROSS

1 Cold war initials
5 They give out cash, initially
9 Dining room furniture
14 Cape ___ (westernmost point of mainland Europe)
15 Sainted pope called "the Great": 2 wds.
16 Having a line of symmetry
17 One of TV's Simpsons
18 Cannonball metal
19 Author C.S.
20 "He loves," in Latin
21 Neat as a pin
23 Acrobatic spring: hyph.
25 Whits or bits
26 Chi follower
27 Norse goddess of fate
28 Some G.I.s
32 NHL's Tikkanen
34 ___ Lanka (Asian island nation)
36 Looks up to
38 Pumpkin seed snack
40 Being annoying
41 Make believe
43 Cholesterol transporter, initially
44 Clock std.
45 Orch. section
46 Attraction
48 Book after Galatians: abbr.
50 Dry
51 ___ the run (dine hastily): 2 wds.
54 Marvel Comics character role for Scarlett Johansson: 2 wds.
59 Hit flies
60 Come from behind
61 "Garfield" character
62 Locale
63 Slightly ahead: 2 wds.
64 Arm part
65 Cries of aversion
66 Ranee's wrap: var.
67 Go after
68 "Hey you!"

DOWN

1 ___ legend (modern-day myth)
2 "Ditto!": 3 wds.
3 Material for casual jotting: 2 wds.
4 Vermin's genus
5 Others, in Latin
6 Ends
7 Young child's word for a cow: 2 wds.
8 Frank of the Rat Pack
9 Anklebone
10 Figure skating jump
11 Largest freshwater lake in Japan
12 Milk in Monaco
13 Apart from this

1	2	3	4	■	5	6	7	8	■	9	10	11	12	13
14				■	15				■	16				
17				■	18				■	19				
20				■	21			22						
23				24	■	25					■	■	■	■
■	■	26			■	27				■	28	29	30	31
32	33		■	34	35		■	36		37				
38			39			■	■	■	40					
41						42	■	43			■	44		
45				■	46		47		■	48	49		■	■
■	■	■	■	50					■	51			52	53
54	55	56	57						58	■	59			
60					■	61				■	62			
63					■	64				■	65			
66					■	67				■	68			

22 Frank and direct
24 Ski trail
28 Water___ (flosser)
29 Halloween hairpieces: 2 wds.
30 Long times to live: abbr.
31 Mil. rank
32 He plays Dr. Foreman on "House"
33 Rockefeller Center muralist
35 Was almost used up: 2 wds.
37 Bobbettes song that begins "One, two, three": 2 wds.
39 Carole King hit, "___ Too Late"
42 Questionable
43 She saves the day
47 Iron ore used in dyeing
49 Refuse (an opportunity): 2 wds.
50 Online call service
52 Presidential affirmations
53 Atom bomb trial: abbr., 2 wds.
54 Frat. members
55 Turner of Tinseltown
56 One of the Sox, e.g.
57 Game with Mr. Boddy
58 Diluted

Solutions

1

S	L	O	W	■	B	I	O	P	S	Y	■	C	B	S
T	A	N	H	■	O	R	N	A	T	E	■	H	E	W
A	C	C	E	P	T	A	T	I	O	N	■	A	A	A
B	E	E	R	Y	■	N	O	N	O	■	D	R	U	B
■	■	■	E	R	A	■	■	E	L	S	E	■	■	■
V	E	R	T	E	B	R	A	■	■	A	N	T	E	■
E	C	H	O	■	Y	U	P	P	I	F	Y	I	N	G
A	L	I	■	E	S	T	H	E	T	E	■	A	D	O
L	A	N	C	A	S	H	I	R	E	■	I	R	O	N
■	T	O	U	R	■	■	D	U	M	B	C	A	N	E
■	■	■	E	L	B	A	■	■	S	U	E	■	■	■
C	U	S	S	■	A	D	A	R	■	S	C	A	L	E
U	R	N	■	H	Y	D	R	O	P	H	O	B	I	A
L	E	O	■	E	O	L	I	T	H	■	L	E	S	S
L	A	W	■	D	U	E	L	E	D	■	D	D	A	Y

2

E	N	N	A	■	U	D	A	Y	■	A	K	R	O	N
L	Y	O	N	■	P	I	T	A	■	T	I	A	G	O
G	A	S	S	■	H	O	U	R	O	F	N	E	E	D
A	L	E	■	B	I	D	S	■	K	I	S	S	E	S
R	A	T	H	O	L	E	■	S	A	R	K	■	■	■
■	■	O	E	I	L	■	L	O	P	S	I	D	E	D
N	U	N	N	S	■	D	E	B	I	T	■	E	R	O
E	P	O	S	■	S	U	P	E	S	■	E	F	T	S
B	I	S	■	L	I	V	E	R	■	S	T	I	E	S
O	N	E	M	E	T	E	R	■	T	H	A	N	■	■
■	■	■	O	A	S	T	■	R	O	U	T	I	N	E
S	I	E	R	R	A	■	W	E	P	T	■	T	E	X
I	N	D	E	N	T	U	R	E	D	■	H	E	L	P
A	R	I	S	E	■	L	E	V	O	■	A	L	L	A
M	I	N	O	R	■	A	N	E	G	■	M	Y	S	T

3

P	A	L	P	■	B	R	A	V	O	■	O	R	E	S
O	C	A	S	■	A	U	X	I	N	■	N	I	L	E
D	E	V	I	T	A	L	I	Z	E	■	I	N	S	T
I	R	E	■	H	I	E	S	■	P	O	C	K	E	T
A	B	S	C	O	N	D	■	P	I	N	E	Y	■	■
■	■	■	E	R	G	■	S	U	E	T	■	D	A	T
D	J	I	N	N	■	J	U	N	C	O	■	I	L	O
H	I	N	T	■	D	A	N	T	E	■	K	N	E	E
A	B	C	■	R	E	B	U	S	■	D	I	K	E	D
L	E	U	■	A	T	O	P	■	V	O	L	■	■	■
■	■	R	O	G	E	T	■	V	A	R	N	I	S	H
S	P	A	R	E	R	■	O	N	U	S	■	D	N	A
A	L	B	A	■	R	E	V	E	L	A	T	I	O	N
M	O	L	T	■	E	R	E	C	T	■	W	O	O	D
E	P	E	E	■	D	A	R	K	S	■	A	M	P	S

4

■	C	O	L	■	A	B	L	E	■	A	V	E	R	■
T	O	D	O	■	A	R	I	D	■	B	E	D	I	M
S	P	E	A	R	H	E	A	D	■	E	N	E	M	A
A	R	O	M	A	■	A	N	O	N	■	O	N	Y	X
R	A	N	■	M	I	C	A	■	E	L	M	■	■	■
■	■	■	R	I	C	H	■	E	W	E	■	A	L	L
T	O	U	P	E	E	■	O	N	T	O	■	F	I	E
W	A	R	M	■	■	F	A	D	■	■	T	R	E	E
I	T	S	■	T	I	C	K	■	O	D	I	O	U	S
G	S	A	■	A	R	C	■	G	H	E	E	■	■	■
■	■	■	P	R	O	■	E	R	S	T	■	O	R	C
A	N	T	I	■	N	O	G	O	■	E	S	S	A	Y
B	U	R	G	S	■	A	R	T	H	R	I	T	I	S
A	N	I	M	E	■	F	E	T	A	■	G	I	S	T
■	S	O	Y	A	■	S	T	O	P	■	N	A	E	■

Solutions

5

	T	I	L		M	P	H			T	E	A	K	S
T	U	B	A		O	R	E		B	O	N	N	I	E
O	P	E	N	D	O	O	R		I	R	V	I	N	E
T	E	R	C	E	N	T	E	N	A	R	Y			
A	L	I	E	N		E	T	A	S			A	R	K
L	O	S	T		I	S	I	S		S	A	R	E	E
				L	A	T	C	H	S	T	R	I	N	G
	C	A	R	O	M				O	U	T	D	O	
R	A	D	I	O	B	E	A	C	O	N				
U	N	A	P	T		A	M	O	K		G	L	U	M
G	E	M			S	T	I	R		C	R	O	N	E
			N	U	T	S	A	N	D	B	O	L	T	S
I	N	C	I	S	E		B	R	A	S	I	L	I	A
V	I	O	L	E	T		L	O	T		N	O	D	S
E	B	B	E	D			E	W	E		S	P	Y	

6

Z	A	I	R	E		A	N	N	E		C	O	O	L
I	N	D	E	X		L	O	O	M		U	R	D	U
G	O	L	F	C	O	U	R	S	E		R	E	I	N
S	A	Y		H	M	M		E	R	E	L	O	N	G
			P	A	I	N		B	A	S	E			
	I	D	E	N	T	I	C	A	L	T	W	I	N	
D	O	I	N	G	S		E	N	D			M	I	L
A	T	O	N	E		M	I	D		D	I	A	N	A
M	A	D			B	E	L		B	U	R	G	O	O
	S	E	L	F	A	S	S	E	R	T	I	O	N	
			O	O	H	S		D	A	I	S			
P	L	A	T	E	A	U		U	S	A		A	B	A
R	O	U	T		M	A	T	C	H	B	O	X	E	S
O	G	R	E		A	G	U	E		L	I	L	A	C
D	E	A	D		S	E	T	S		E	L	E	M	I

7

C	O	R	K		U	S	E		S	C	O	U	T	S
B	O	O	N		R	U	N		M	A	G	N	E	T
S	H	O	O	T	I	N	G	G	A	L	L	E	R	Y
		F	B	I		B	R	O	S		E	A	R	L
E	E	R		E	R	A		S	H	H		S	O	U
T	R	A	N	S	I	T		H	E	I	F	E	R	S
N	I	C	E		P	H	D		R	N	A			
A	N	K	H	S		E	R	G		D	U	P	E	D
			R	A	P		Y	U	P		N	I	K	E
S	P	O	U	S	A	L		E	S	C	A	P	E	E
H	A	P		S	P	A		R	I	O		E	S	P
A	L	T	O		O	M	E	N		D	A	L		
R	A	I	L	R	O	A	D	S	T	A	T	I	O	N
E	C	C	L	E	S		G	E	E		O	N	C	E
S	E	S	A	M	E		E	Y	E		M	E	A	D

8

E	Y	C	K		H	D	T	V			I	N	D	S
R	O	A	N		A	R	I	E			G	E	R	T
S	U	P	E	R	M	O	D	E	L		U	R	E	Y
T	R	E	E	L	I	N	E		I	N	A	F	I	X
			P	E	T	E		L	E	A	N			
A	L	I	A	S	E	S		I	D	S	A	Y	S	O
L	A	R	D	S			A	C	E	H		I	O	C
O	W	E	S		O	F	F	E	R		M	E	R	C
H	E	N		A	G	A	R			M	A	L	T	A
A	D	E	P	T	L	Y		Q	U	O	N	D	A	M
			I	R	A	E		A	N	N	E			
O	S	T	E	A	L		I	N	S	T	A	N	C	E
M	A	R	C		A	L	L	T	H	E	T	I	M	E
E	V	I	E			E	S	A	I		E	M	A	G
N	E	B	S			R	A	S	P		R	S	S	S

Solutions

9

W	O	N	G		A	V	E	C		D	E	A	F	
A	N	O	S		F	A	S	O		E	N	C	L	
R	E	M	E	M	B	R	A	N	C	E	D	A	Y	
	T	A	V	I				M	O	R	O	C	C	O
V	I	D	E	O	A	R	C	A	D	E		I	A	L
I	M	I	N		M	I	L	N	E		P	A	S	A
A	E	C		B	A	L	I			R	U	S	T	Y
			R	O	S	E	P	E	T	A	L			
A	T	O	N	Y			A	L	O	E		B	P	S
L	A	V	A		K	A	R	O	L		I	L	L	S
E	K	E		R	E	C	T	I	L	I	N	E	A	R
F	E	R	M	E	N	T				D	A	M	N	
	O	D	D	S	O	N	F	A	V	O	R	I	T	E
	F	U	S	E		O	H	N	O		U	S	A	C
	F	E	E	T		W	A	A	C		T	H	R	U

10

A	H	E	M		G	A	R	R		E	A	T	I	T
L	Y	R	A		U	F	O	S		T	R	A	C	E
O	E	I	L		I	R	A	S		H	A	L	A	L
U	N	C	L	E	T	O	M	S	C	A	B	I	N	
	A	K	E	L	A	S			O	N	S			
			A	I	R		D	B	L	S		W	S	W
S	N	O	B	S		C	I	A	O		S	O	L	A
T	H	E	L	E	M	O	N	D	R	O	P	K	I	D
E	R	D	E		A	R	O	D		D	E	E	M	S
S	A	S		R	N	A	S		H	D	L			
			G	I	G			P	O	L	L	O	I	
	I	H	A	V	E	N	T	A	N	Y	I	D	E	A
P	L	A	Y	A		A	R	I	E		N	O	V	A
S	K	I	L	L		P	I	N	S		G	R	E	S
S	A	G	E	S		A	S	E	T		S	S	R	S

11

G	R	A	S	P			R	E	A	P		K	E	A
A	U	D	I	O		R	I	F	L	E		I	L	L
S	H	O	R	T	L	I	S	T	E	D		R	I	G
H	R	S		H	Y	P	E	S		D	H	O	T	I
			I	O	N				E	L	E	V	E	N
C	A	N	N	O	N	F	O	D	D	E	R			
A	B	A	C	K		O	N	A	I	R		P	H	I
B	L	A	H		P	O	I	N	T		B	E	A	R
S	E	N		D	O	L	C	E		P	L	A	N	K
			P	U	R	S	E	S	T	R	I	N	G	S
I	M	B	I	B	E				Y	E	P			
C	O	R	G	I		S	O	A	R	S		S	K	I
T	I	E		O	P	E	N	M	O	U	T	H	E	D
U	R	N		U	S	E	U	P		M	A	I	N	E
S	E	T		S	I	P	S			E	X	P	O	S

12

A	L	O	H	A		I	V	E	Y		G	P	A	S
C	O	C	O	A		D	I	N	A		I	O	L	E
A	U	T	O	M	A	T	E	D	T	E	L	L	E	R
D	I	E	D		K	A	T	O		E	D	I	C	T
S	E	T		S	I	G	N		B	R	A	C		
			C	I	O		A	M	O	Y		E	M	U
S	C	O	R	N		I	M	A	N		N	C	I	S
M	A	R	T	H	A	S	V	I	N	E	Y	A	R	D
I	M	P	S		M	A	E	O		B	E	R	E	T
T	A	H		P	I	T	T		O	B	S			
		A	L	A	E		E	A	T	S		G	A	D
I	O	N	I	C		O	R	S	O		T	O	N	E
S	H	A	K	E	S	H	A	K	E	S	H	A	K	E
L	O	G	E		A	N	N	I		P	O	P	U	P
S	H	E	D		B	O	S	N		A	M	E	S	S

Solutions

13

A	M	A	D	O		S	P	E	E	D		U	R	B
S	E	W	E	R		P	E	R	D	U		N	O	L
C	E	R	T	I	F	I	C	A	T	E		E	T	A
I	T	Y		G	O	E	S			T	I	V	O	S
			L	A	I	R		G	U	T	L	E	S	S
E	X	H	U	M	E		T	U	R	E	E	N		
L	E	O	X	I		R	A	P	I	D		B	A	M
A	N	C	E		R	O	M	P	S		M	A	R	E
L	A	K		C	A	S	E	Y		O	K	R	A	S
		E	V	O	K	E	D		O	P	T	S	T	O
S	A	Y	W	H	E	N		A	L	E	G			
L	A	P	S	E			E	D	E	N		P	I	S
I	N	U		R	A	I	S	E	A	S	T	I	N	K
C	D	C		E	S	T	A	B		U	H	U	R	A
E	E	K		D	L	I	S	T		P	O	S	I	T

14

	D	A	W		B	B	O	Y		H	E	L	D	
T	I	C	E		N	A	N	U		A	M	O	U	R
I	D	E	A		A	N	O	A		V	I	B	E	S
P	Y	R	R	H	I	C		N	L	E		E	L	S
T	A	B	O	O					I	N	D			
			U	P	I		G	B	E		U	T	N	E
E	M	O	T	I	O	N	A	L			H	O	A	X
L	B	J			S	A	L	V	E			G	T	O
L	A	O	S			G	O	D	I	S	G	O	O	D
E	S	S	E		M	A	P		N	E	A			
			D	F	C					A	G	E	R	S
L	U	S		A	A	E		O	I	L	S	P	O	T
G	R	A	M	M		L	U	C	E		T	O	L	U
A	L	B	E	E		I	S	T	S		E	D	E	N
	S	E	E	D		S	N	O	T		R	E	O	

15

S	I	T	U	P			I	M	P		D	O	C	
O	L	I	V	E	R		N	I	L		A	P	E	R
C	O	M	E	T	O		S	N	O	W	L	I	N	E
		E	A	S	T	S	O	U	T	H	E	A	S	T
A	D	Z			C	A	F	E		O	T	T	E	R
S	H	O	A	L		R	A	N	K		H	E	R	O
P	A	N	T	Y	G	I	R	D	L	E				
	L	E	M	O	N				A	D	A	G	E	
			N	A	T	I	O	N	A	L	I	S	T	
S	C	A	D		W	E	N	T		M	A	M	A	S
L	O	S	E	S		S	W	I	G			C	U	P
U	N	S	P	E	C	T	A	C	U	L	A	R		
G	R	I	T	T	I	E	R		S	O	L	A	C	E
S	A	S	H		T	E	D		T	A	L	C	U	M
	D	I	S		E	S	S			F	Y	K	E	S

16

K	E	G		T	A	C	H		A	S	H	A	M	E
O	N	E		A	G	H	A		D	I	A	L	O	G
A	T	M		D	U	E	L		M	E	R	I	N	O
L	A	I	S	S	E	Z	F	A	I	R	E			
A	I	N	U					S	T	R	E	A	K	S
S	L	I	M	E		M	A	S		A	M	N	I	O
			A	D	D	E	D	U	P			T	E	L
N	E	O	C	O	N	S	E	R	V	A	T	I	V	E
A	R	P			A	S	P	E	C	T	S			
I	N	E	R	T		I	T	D		E	A	S	E	D
F	E	D	E	R	A	L					R	I	P	E
			P	O	L	Y	T	H	E	I	S	T	I	C
T	R	Y	O	U	T		H	O	R	N		U	Z	I
S	H	E	R	P	A		A	M	O	K		P	O	D
P	O	S	T	E	R		N	O	S	Y		S	A	E

Solutions

17

V	I	M	S		A	J	A	R		E	S	S	I	E
O	M	O	O		S	O	R	A		S	A	H	I	B
I	P	A	D		S	P	A	N		P	L	A	N	B
C	O	N	S	T	E	L	L	A	T	I	O	N		
E	S	E		I	T	I		R	E	E		G	M	A
S	T	R	A	P		N	A	I	A	D		H	E	W
			G	S	A		R	S	S		A	A	A	A
S	T	O	R	Y	B	O	O	K	E	N	D	I	N	G
L	I	L	A		L	U	M		R	E	I			
A	M	D		D	E	T	A	T		W	O	U	N	D
Y	E	H		A	S	T		A	B	A		N	E	O
		A	S	H	T	O	N	K	U	T	C	H	E	R
L	I	B	E	L		S	E	E	R		R	U	D	I
A	M	I	C	I		E	T	T	E		I	N	L	A
G	O	T	T	A		A	S	O	N		T	H	E	N

18

S	E	U	S	S		L	A	M	P		A	E	R	Y
A	S	N	I	T		A	C	A	I		F	L	E	A
R	O	C	K	A	N	D	R	Y	E		I	T	O	R
	L	A	H	T	I		O	N	R	E	C	O	R	D
				A	C	H		T	I	D	I	N	G	S
S	I	M	O	L	E	O	N		S	N	O			
I	L	E	S		S	R	A			A	N	A	I	L
B	R	A	C		T	A	S	E	D		A	M	T	S
S	E	T	A	N			A	A	U		D	E	B	T
			R	Y	S		L	U	M	M	O	X	E	S
S	T	E	W	P	O	T		S	B	A				
L	A	P	I	D	A	R	Y		O	D	D	E	R	
O	E	I	L		R	O	L	L	S	R	O	Y	C	E
A	B	C	D		E	P	E	E		I	D	E	A	L
N	O	S	E		D	E	M	Y		D	O	R	S	A

19

M	A	P	S		D	A	R	I	N	G		D	D	E
Y	E	O	W		I	C	E	S	A	W		O	O	P
T	R	O	I		G	E	N	E	R	A		U	T	A
H	O	R	S	E	S	H	O	E	C	R	A	B		
			H	O	I						S	L	A	V
A	N	C		S	N	O	B	S		U	S	E	M	E
B	E	L	T		T	R	A	P		D	U	P	E	S
S	W	O	R	D	O	F	D	A	M	O	C	L	E	S
E	T	U	I	S		E	A	T	A		H	A	R	E
N	O	D	T	O		O	T	E	R	I		Y	S	L
T	Y	C	O						Z	A	C			
		O	N	E	I	N	A	M	I	L	L	I	O	N
C	I	V		S	N	A	P	U	P		I	F	N	I
O	D	E		O	R	G	A	N	A		V	A	I	N
S	S	R		S	E	A	L	I	N		E	T	T	E

20

A	S	N	O		N	E	U	R		A	M	I	G	A
I	T	E	N		O	N	M	E		C	A	G	E	S
S	A	F	E		R	E	D	B	U	T	T	O	N	S
	R	E	S	O	W			O	L	E	S	T	R	A
A	T	R	I	A		D	O	O	N			O	E	D
P	E	T	E	F	O	U	N	T	A	I	N			
I	D	I			R	E	A			S	E	T	I	
	I	T	C	O	U	L	D	H	A	P	P	E	N	
	N	I	C	O			I	I	N			A	D	E
			S	M	O	K	E	D	S	A	L	M	O	N
T	I	N			D	O	T	E		C	A	S	C	A
A	P	O	G	E	E	S			T	R	U	T	H	
L	O	V	E	Y	D	O	V	E	Y		R	E	I	D
I	D	A	R	E		V	I	E	R		E	R	N	E
A	S	E	E	D		O	N	N	O		L	S	A	T

Solutions

21

E	A	V	E		H	A	S	A		B	L	U	S	H
T	Z	A	R		I	H	A	D		E	A	S	T	S
A	T	C	O		T	A	K	E	S	A	P	A	R	T
P	E	U		M	R	I	S		E	G	S			
E	C	U	A	D	O	R		T	A	L	E	N	T	S
		M	A	S	C		A	A	R	E		A	A	E
	L	P	N		K	O	V	I	C		W	I	R	E
M	E	A	D		B	R	I	T	H		O	L	I	D
C	E	C	E		O	N	L	O	W		M	C	Q	
C	L	K		S	T	O	A		A	B	E	L		
C	A	S	S	A	T	T		I	R	O	N	I	E	S
			W	Y	O		C	T	R	S		P	P	P
M	I	X	E	D	M	E	D	I	A		S	P	C	A
A	D	L	A	I		P	E	N	N		L	E	O	N
G	E	S	T	E		I	F	A	T		O	R	T	S

22

C	A	E	N		G	U	A	R	S		S	T	U	D
O	R	C	A		E	S	P	O	O		N	Y	R	O
H	E	R	E	A	N	D	N	O	W		O	P	A	H
O	S	U		L	E	T	E	M		O	O	O	L	A
			C	U	T		A	B	U	Z	Z			
D	Y	N	A	M	I	C		A	M	O	E	B	A	S
R	U	E	S		C	A	D		A	N	A	R	C	H
A	K	I	S	S		F	I	G		E	L	A	T	E
P	O	L	I	C	E		R	N	S		A	V	I	D
E	N	S	U	R	E	D		P	A	T	R	O	N	S
			S	O	L	E	D		R	O	M			
M	I	X	C	D		T	E	D	D	Y		F	E	M
E	N	O	L		H	A	R	R	I	S	B	U	R	G
S	K	U	A		T	I	M	O	N		Y	M	I	R
O	A	T	Y		S	L	O	P	E		S	E	E	S

23

C	O	G	S		F	R	U	G		F	A	K	I	R
A	N	A	D		L	I	R	E		A	M	I	N	O
R	A	D	I	O	E	D	I	T		R	O	N	C	O
O	I	D		M	D	S		M	A	G		T	A	S
B	R	A	G	A			R	E	F	O	R	E	S	T
			O	R	A	R	E		I	N	A			
I	N	N	E	R	T	U	B	E		E	I	D	E	R
N	I	M	S		L	E	E	Z	A		N	O	S	E
G	L	E	A	M		S	C	R	E	W	B	A	L	L
			P	Y	M		C	A	C	A	O			
S	W	E	E	T	P	E	A			S	W	A	M	P
A	H	A		R	S	A		O	P	P		U	S	A
R	O	S	I	E		R	O	A	D	S	I	G	N	S
A	L	E	T	A		P	U	R	A		D	E	B	T
H	E	L	O	T		S	I	S	S		O	R	C	A

24

H	I	K	E			L	I	S				A	K	A
O	D	E	S		P	I	N	U	P		S	I	A	N
P	O	R	T	M	A	N	T	E	A	U	W	O	R	D
E	L	F		E	Y	E	R		P	S	A	L	M	
			S	T	E	N	O		O	S	T	I	A	
	S	T	A	R	E	S		F	O	R				
A	L	I	B	I			C	O	S		H	E	R	O
D	I	R	E	C	T	O	R	G	E	N	E	R	A	L
O	D	O	R		R	U	T			A	L	G	I	D
				W	E	T		M	A	M	M	O	N	
	L	A	M	I	A		R	A	G	E	S			
	O	B	I	T	S		A	R	I	L		T	O	O
P	S	Y	C	H	O	A	N	A	L	Y	Z	I	N	G
E	S	S	E		N	I	E	C	E		E	L	U	L
G	Y	M				L	E	A				E	L	S	E

Solutions

25

T	B	A	R	■	S	L	U	E	■	T	I	N	A	■
H	A	L	O	■	P	I	P	S	■	E	N	E	M	Y
A	T	T	A	■	O	T	R	O	■	E	D	G	A	R
W	H	I	M	S	I	C	A	L	■	P	O	E	T	S
■	■	■	■	E	L	H	I	■	L	E	O	V	I	■
■	B	O	S	N	■	I	S	S	U	E	R	■	■	■
C	A	N	T	O	S	■	E	U	R	■	P	S	S	T
O	C	C	U	R	T	O	■	R	E	T	O	R	T	S
S	H	E	D	■	I	O	C	■	R	I	O	T	E	R
■	■	■	M	I	C	M	A	C	■	A	L	A	S	■
■	W	A	U	G	H	■	P	A	A	R	■	■	■	■
R	O	L	F	E	■	E	S	T	R	A	N	G	E	S
D	R	I	F	T	■	S	I	S	I	■	O	R	L	Y
A	S	C	I	I	■	A	Z	U	L	■	P	I	A	F
■	T	E	N	T	■	S	E	P	S	■	E	M	M	Y

26

H	O	U	R	■	N	A	N	U	■	A	S	S	A	M
O	H	S	O	■	I	C	A	N	■	L	E	T	G	O
O	A	H	U	■	L	A	I	D	■	O	T	E	R	O
P	R	E	S	S	E	D	F	O	R	T	I	M	E	■
E	A	R	T	H	■	■	S	E	E	■	■	A	E	R
R	S	S	■	A	H	S	■	R	O	O	T	R	O	T
■	■	■	S	W	E	P	T	■	■	P	A	I	N	E
■	■	W	I	N	B	Y	A	F	L	U	K	E	■	■
P	A	E	S	E	■	■	P	H	Y	L	A	■	■	■
U	G	L	I	E	S	T	■	A	S	E	■	I	T	O
F	I	S	■	■	U	E	Y	■	■	N	I	G	E	L
■	T	H	E	D	E	F	I	A	N	T	O	N	E	S
T	A	M	L	A	■	L	E	V	O	■	N	O	D	E
A	T	E	A	T	■	O	L	I	O	■	I	R	U	N
D	O	N	N	A	■	N	D	A	K	■	C	E	P	S

27

T	S	E	■	K	A	T	Y	■	K	N	E	L	L	S
U	L	M	■	I	L	Y	A	■	N	O	D	E	A	L
B	U	M	S	T	E	E	R	■	O	R	A	T	O	R
B	R	E	A	T	H	E	■	C	W	T	S	■	■	■
■	■	■	U	S	O	■	R	A	S	H	N	E	S	S
■	D	S	L	■	U	M	B	R	A	■	E	N	O	L
N	I	E	T	Z	S	C	H	E	■	T	R	A	L	A
E	S	C	■	E	E	N	■	S	A	N	■	T	O	N
U	P	O	N	E	■	A	T	T	E	N	D	I	N	G
R	E	N	E	■	O	L	E	O	S	■	A	C	S	■
O	L	D	W	O	R	L	D	■	O	H	M	■	■	■
■	■	■	G	A	M	Y	■	S	P	I	N	D	L	E
E	L	P	A	S	O	■	S	L	I	P	S	H	O	D
T	O	O	T	E	R	■	S	O	A	P	■	A	R	Y
C	L	E	E	S	E	■	I	T	N	O	■	L	Y	S

28

H	A	E	C	■	L	A	R	A	M	■	A	S	E	A
A	S	N	O	■	A	M	A	T	I	■	V	E	R	B
S	I	G	N	■	I	N	S	T	S	■	A	E	R	O
■	F	R	E	U	D	I	A	N	S	L	I	P	S	■
■	■	■	H	S	I	A	■	■	O	I	L	■	■	■
P	O	T	E	E	N	■	P	T	U	I	■	D	I	D
A	N	W	A	R	■	G	O	E	R	■	S	E	G	O
S	H	E	D	S	O	M	E	L	I	G	H	T	O	N
T	O	R	S	■	P	E	T	E	■	A	A	R	O	N
A	T	E	■	F	E	N	S	■	A	L	K	E	N	E
■	■	■	O	E	N	■	■	I	S	L	E	■	■	■
■	S	O	P	H	I	E	S	C	H	O	I	C	E	■
D	A	R	T	■	N	G	A	I	O	■	T	A	E	L
I	N	T	I	■	G	A	Y	E	R	■	U	R	E	A
F	I	S	C	■	S	N	A	R	E	■	P	S	S	T

Solutions

29

S	P	A	S		H	I	J	A	B		C	O	D	A
C	O	L	L		A	N	I	M	E		O	N	U	S
H	O	B	O		K	O	L	A	S		R	O	O	K
E	L	E	P	H	A	N	T	S	E	A	R			
M	E	D	E	A				S	E	R	E	N	E	R
A	D	O		R	A	S	H		M	E	L	O	D	Y
			E	S	P	I	A	L			A	I	D	E
	M	O	T	H	E	R	C	O	U	N	T	R	Y	
E	I	R	E			S	E	T	T	E	E			
M	E	T	R	O	S		K	I	E	V		L	A	B
U	N	S	N	A	P	S				E	P	O	D	E
			A	F	R	O	A	M	E	R	I	C	A	N
D	H	A	L		U	L	C	E	R		T	A	G	S
Y	O	W	L		C	O	I	N	S		O	L	I	O
E	E	L	Y		E	N	D	U	E		N	E	O	N

30

A	Z	O	T	H		E	T	N	A		B	A	R	K
M	U	N	R	O		R	E	A	P		A	L	O	E
I	N	S	U	R	A	N	C	E	P	O	L	I	C	Y
D	I	E	T		N	I	H		O	A	T			
E	S	T	H	E	T	E		E	S	K	I	M	O	S
			F	I	E			V	I	S	C	E	R	A
	S	L	U	R		S	P	A	T			R	A	T
	T	E	L	E	P	H	O	N	E	C	A	L	L	
G	O	A			T	U	T	S		U	S	E	S	
S	A	F	F	R	O	N			O	R	T			
A	S	Y	L	U	M	S		M	A	L	E	F	I	C
			Y	E	A		M	A	R		R	U	D	E
F	O	U	R	D	I	M	E	N	S	I	O	N	A	L
I	N	T	O		N	A	M	E		R	I	G	H	T
T	O	E	D		E	G	O	S		A	D	I	O	S

31

M	C	C	V		P	A	R	A			S	C	A	T
A	L	U	I		I	R	A	B	U		R	I	M	S
R	U	B	S		N	O	F	O	R		I	V	O	R
V	E	R	T	I	G	O		R	N	A	S			
		E	A	R	P		G	I	S	H		E	P	A
C	U	P		S	O	B	I	G		E	E	L	E	R
U	S	O	S		N	O	V	I		M	Y	B	A	D
S	A	R	K		G	L	E	N	S		R	O	L	E
P	U	T	O	N		L	S	A	T		E	W	E	N
I	S	E	R	E		W	I	L	E	Y		G	S	T
D	A	R		T	E	E	N		L	O	U	R		
			E	T	R	E		O	L	D	B	E	A	N
T	I	N	S		I	V	A	N	A		O	A	K	Y
U	T	E	P		N	I	P	I	T		A	S	I	P
A	S	H	Y			L	A	N	E		T	E	N	D

32

B	A	B	E		S	A	N	S		S	T	O	M	A
O	C	A	S		C	L	O	P		T	O	P	I	C
N	I	L	S		A	P	S	E		E	R	A	S	E
U	N	D	E	R	T	H	E	W	E	A	T	H	E	R
S	I	S		E	T	A			A	D	S			
			B	A	Y		N	A	V	Y		C	H	A
I	S	A	A	C		M	O	L	E		C	O	A	X
L	I	G	H	T	N	I	N	G	S	T	R	I	K	E
K	N	I	T		I	D	E	A		A	U	R	A	L
S	E	N		O	M	I	T		B	U	D			
			S	I	B			C	E	P		C	I	A
S	U	P	P	L	Y	A	N	D	D	E	M	A	N	D
I	L	I	A	C		F	O	R	E		O	L	L	A
A	N	T	R	A		A	V	O	W		C	L	E	G
L	A	T	E	N		R	A	M	S		K	I	T	E

Solutions

33

A	R	O		S	H	A	S	T	A		O	C	T	S
M	E	M		P	I	G	P	E	N		D	U	R	A
I	N	A	D	E	Q	U	A	T	E		E	B	A	Y
S	E	R	A	C		E	R	E		B	R	E	W	S
H	E	R	N	I	A		E	S	A	U		S	L	O
			G	F	L	A	T		I	F	A	T		
S	O	U		I	T	C	H		N	F	L	E	R	S
B	A	S	I	C		R	E	D		A	S	A	H	I
A	K	E	L	A	S		D	E	A	L		K	O	N
		L	O	L	O		E	L	R	O	D			
E	S	E		L	A	C	T		S	W	E	L	L	S
P	O	S	E	Y		A	A	E		I	S	E	E	A
I	P	S	A		P	R	I	S	O	N	C	A	M	P
C	U	L	T		O	B	L	O	N	G		H	M	O
S	P	Y	S		M	O	S	S	E	S		Y	E	R

34

I	L	K	A		A	C	H	E		M	C	R	A	E
T	A	E	L		C	H	O	Y		T	H	E	R	M
I	V	Y	L	E	A	G	U	E		V	I	T	R	O
			A	D	D		R	O	D		S	U	E	T
A	M	A	T	I			I	N	A	S	E	N	S	E
R	E	D	S	T	A	R			V	A	L	E	T	
A	C	U	E		N	O	G	G	I	N				
	H	E	A	R	T	P	O	U	N	D	I	N	G	
				T	I	E	T	A	C		N	O	O	N
	R	E	N	E	W			M	I	S	F	I	R	E
P	A	L	I	S	A	D	E			Y	O	D	E	L
L	I	M	N		R	U	R		M	F	R			
I	L	I	E	D		P	A	T	T	Y	M	E	L	T
C	E	R	T	S		E	T	O	N		O	R	L	Y
A	D	A	Y	S		R	O	W	S		N	E	B	S

35

	V	A	L		G	R	A	H	A	M		B	I	P
B	A	L	E		L	O	V	E	T	O		A	R	S
A	R	O	D		O	B	E	R	O	N		D	E	S
S	I	N	G	A	P	O	R	E		T	O	M		
R	E	S	E	W					S	A	B	O	T	S
A	D	O		A	V	A		U	N	G	L	U	E	D
			P	I	A	N	O	L	A		I	T	S	I
	T	H	A	T	S	N	O	T	R	I	G	H	T	
N	E	A	T		S	U	P	R	E	M	E			
I	L	L	E	G	A	L		A	D	E		A	F	T
H	E	F	N	E	R					T	Y	L	E	R
		M	S	N		E	A	S	Y	A	S	P	I	E
B	O	O		D	O	C	I	L	E		T	A	N	K
A	M	O		E	S	C	R	O	W		A	C	T	S
R	E	N		R	O	O	S	T	S		D	A	S	

36

	A	C	A	N		M	S	R	P		E	G	A	N
A	S	O	L	O		O	P	A	H		V	E	R	T
M	A	R	I	E		M	A	N	A		I	N	N	E
I	N	D	E	X	C	A	R	D	S		L	U	I	S
			N	I	H			D	E	A	D	S	E	T
B	L	I	S	T	E	R	S		I	W	O			
O	P	S			R	O	O	S		A	E	I	O	U
S	N	A	K	E	I	N	T	H	E	G	R	A	S	S
N	S	Y	N	C		I	T	O	R			G	S	N
			U	H	F		O	P	E	N	D	O	O	R
E	N	A	C	T	E	D			C	E	E			
N	O	C	K		R	U	N	S	T	O	S	E	E	D
E	L	U	L		U	P	O	N		C	I	N	C	O
M	A	T	E		L	E	V	O		O	C	C	U	R
A	N	E	S		E	D	I	T		N	A	Y	S	

Solutions

37

M	O	P	E		M	O	O	T		C	H	I	D	
E	V	E	N		A	D	A	R		H	E	T	U	P
S	E	R	E	N	G	E	T	I		O	L	L	A	S
A	R	P		A	G	O		B	A	C	I	L	L	I
S	T	E	P	S	O	N		U	N	T	O			
		T	H	A	T		S	T	O	A		C	A	L
C	A	R	O	L		M	E	A	N	W	H	I	L	E
O	M	A	N			E	A	R			O	R	T	S
L	I	T	E	R	A	L	L	Y		L	O	C	O	S
A	R	E		E	G	O	S		L	I	E	U		
			S	P	U	D		B	A	B	Y	I	S	H
R	E	S	C	U	E	R		U	T	E		T	W	O
A	V	A	I	L		A	P	R	I	L	F	O	O	L
G	I	R	O	S		M	A	I	N		L	U	R	E
	L	I	N	E		A	N	N	O		U	S	E	D

38

A	G	A	N	A		T	I	O	S		A	S	A	P
M	A	C	E	D		I	S	N	O		L	A	D	S
C	O	R	D	O	N	B	L	E	U		U	N	I	S
S	L	Y		R	I	I	S		R	A	M	J	E	T
			M	I	L	A		O	M	I	N	O	U	S
S	A	T	I	N	S		C	R	A	N	I	A		
G	R	E	G	G		B	E	E	S	T		Q	I	N
A	L	A	S		A	L	L	A	H		R	U	N	A
S	O	R		S	T	A	I	D		R	E	I	M	S
		S	C	O	T	I	A		S	O	N	N	E	T
S	C	H	O	L	A	R		U	P	S	A			
T	H	E	D	O	G		B	R	E	W		D	A	H
I	L	E	D		I	C	E	I	C	E	B	A	B	Y
R	O	T	L		R	I	T	A		L	A	W	E	D
S	E	S	E		L	E	A	H		L	Y	N	D	E

39

S	A	F	E		T	A	C	O	S		O	M	S	K
E	N	O	L		A	M	P	U	L		B	E	N	E
W	O	R	L	D	W	E	A	R	Y		E	T	A	L
N	A	M		U	S	E				A	L	O	F	T
		U	N	C	E	R	E	M	O	N	I	O	U	S
S	P	L	I	T		S	N	O	R	E				
P	E	A	T	S			D	O	G	W	O	O	D	
A	N	T	E		S	A	L	T	Y		C	R	A	G
	S	E	R	V	I	L	E			S	E	A	M	S
				E	G	E	S	T		W	A	N	N	A
H	Y	P	O	T	H	E	S	I	Z	I	N	G		
B	A	R	B	S				E	L	M		U	S	A
O	H	I	O		C	O	M	P	O	S	I	T	O	R
M	O	V	E		A	W	A	I	T		N	A	S	A
B	O	Y	S		P	E	O	N	Y		K	N	O	B

40

C	C	C		S	C	A	B			S	T	O	U	P
H	A	O		H	A	M	A	S		T	O	R	S	O
U	R	L		A	S	O	R	T		A	W	M	A	N
R	E	A	D	D	S		B	R	A	I	N	E	R	D
R	E	D	E	Y	E		E	A	G	R	E			
O	N	A	N		T	A	R	P	S			D	O	M
			I	N	T	R	O			S	O	C	K	S
Q	U	A	R	T	E	R	F	I	N	A	L	I	S	T
R	I	C	O	H			S	T	E	E	D			
S	E	C			I	M	E	T	A		S	O	H	O
			N	E	G	E	V		T	E	A	M	U	P
R	I	G	A	T	O	N	I		N	L	W	E	S	T
E	L	U	D	E		S	L	I	E	R		A	H	I
F	E	L	I	X		A	L	L	S	O		R	E	M
S	T	P	A	T			E	A	S	Y		A	S	A

Solutions

41

L	A	N	G	E		S	O	T	T	O		C	B	C
S	T	O	O	D		A	S	C	A	N		O	O	H
A	C	U	P	U	N	C	T	U	R	E		N	W	A
T	O	S	H		O	S	E		M	A	N	N	E	R
			E	A	T			D	A	L	A	I		
	P	A	R	T	I	A	L	E	C	L	I	P	S	E
J	I	M		I	N	S	E	T			A	T	O	N
E	N	A	C	T		T	V	A		E	D	I	F	Y
T	O	L	L			H	E	I	N	Z		O	T	O
E	N	G	A	G	E	M	E	N	T	R	I	N	G	
		A	R	U	B	A			E	A	N			
D	E	M	O	T	E		I	O	S		F	A	D	E
U	L	A		T	R	U	T	H	T	E	L	L	E	R
M	E	T		E	L	M	O	S		M	O	I	R	A
A	M	E		R	E	P	R	O		I	W	A	N	T

42

A	T	E	A	S	E		M	B	E	S		M	O	A
C	H	I	N	U	P		I	A	M	A		I	C	U
R	E	G	I	M	E		A	R	M	Y	A	N	T	S
O	O	H		M	E	M	O	R	Y		P	D	A	S
		T	E	E		E	W	E		A	I	O	L	I
E	N	T	E	R	E	D		L	O	M	A	N		
M	A	R	G		D	I	P	O	D	Y		E	R	S
I	M	A	S		E	C	A	R	D		I	S	I	T
T	E	C		S	M	I	D	G	E		S	P	C	A
		K	A	R	A	N		A	R	I	O	S	O	S
O	A	T	H	S		A	N	N		D	N	A		
I	G	A	S		E	L	I	S	H	A		N	E	C
N	A	P	O	L	E	O	N		I	H	A	D	T	O
G	R	E		E	R	I	N		T	O	R	Q	U	E
O	S	S		R	O	L	Y		A	S	K	S	I	N

43

C	O	V	E		R	S	S	S		A	S	P	E	R
A	S	E	T		A	T	I	E		A	T	A	L	E
D	I	S	C		H	O	T	E		A	J	U	G	A
G	E	T	S	A	R	O	U	N	D		O	L	I	D
E	R	R		H	A	L			A	T	H	A	N	D
		Y	E	A	H		I	N	M	E	N			
H	E	M	I			S	P	O	U	T		I	T	N
B	L	A	N	K	E	T	A	P	P	R	O	V	A	L
O	O	N		I	R	E	N	E			C	Y	M	E
			A	K	I	R	A		Z	E	A	L		
S	E	P	T	I	C			B	O	A		E	O	S
A	X	E	R		H	U	D	S	O	N	H	A	W	K
M	A	C	A	O		P	R	I	M		A	G	N	I
B	L	O	C	S		D	E	D	E		S	U	E	T
A	T	S	E	A		O	W	E	D		H	E	R	S

44

C	L	A	M	P		E	N	L		O	A	S	I	S
C	E	S	A	R		M	O	A		P	I	N	T	A
I	S	T	L	E		I	T	I	N	E	R	A	N	T
		E	A	C	H		I	C	E		E	G	O	S
C	U	R	R	I	E	D	F	A	V	O	R			
A	P	O		S	L	R		L	A	O		Y	T	D
B	L	I	N		G	A	T			O	N	E	O	R
M	A	D	A	S	A	M	A	R	C	H	H	A	R	E
E	T	A	P	E			N	I	H		A	R	P	S
N	E	L		E	A	T		S	L	O		I	O	S
			C	R	O	S	S	C	O	U	N	T	R	Y
I	L	E	R		K	E	W		E	R	I	C		
S	U	P	E	R	S	T	A	R		M	E	H	T	A
A	N	I	M	E		S	M	U		A	C	E	I	N
K	E	S	E	Y		E	I	S		N	E	S	T	S

Solutions

45

I	O	T	A			U	R	G	E			V	A	R
N	L	E	R		C	H	A	R	O		P	E	N	A
D	E	R	M		A	F	L	A	C		U	R	N	S
C	O	Z	E	N	S			T	E	A	M	S	U	P
		A	N	I	S	E		A	N	O	M	A	L	Y
	T	R	I	N	A	R	Y		E	K	E			
L	E	I	A		T	I	A	S		I	L	I	U	M
G	E	M			T	E	N	O	R			M	S	T
A	S	A	H	I		S	K	U	A		U	P	S	A
			U	L	E		S	C	I	S	S	O	R	
R	E	A	R	E	N	D		I	N	N	E	R		
O	N	S	T	A	G	E			H	A	L	T	E	D
A	U	E	L		L	A	I	L	A		E	A	V	E
C	R	E	E		U	N	F	I	T		S	N	I	P
H	E	D			T	E	S	T			S	T	E	T

46

B	O	D		S	P	O	T	S			E	M	A	G
B	C	E		T	E	E	U	P		O	P	E	R	E
C	O	V	E	R	N	O	T	E		H	I	T	A	T
	N	E	X	U	S		T	A	X	I	C	A	B	S
U	N	L	O	C	K		I	K	E			L	I	B
T	O	O		K	E	S			N	A	Y	S	A	Y
A	R	P	S			O	L	E	O	L	E			
		S	T	A	R	W	I	T	N	E	S	S		
			E	D	E	N	I	C			M	K	T	G
E	L	A	N	D	S			H	E	M		U	I	E
T	I	L			E	S	G		R	E	A	L	M	S
H	O	L	D	D	E	A	R		O	R	A	L	B	
I	N	U	R	E		B	O	O	T	L	A	C	E	S
C	E	D	A	R		R	A	D	I	O		A	R	T
S	L	E	W			E	N	A	C	T		P	S	P

47

E	R	S	T		S	P	A	M		B	A	R	G	E
S	O	L	O		M	I	N	I		I	B	E	A	M
P	A	U	L		O	R	T	S		G	E	S	T	S
I	R	R	E	C	L	A	I	M	A	B	L	E		
E	E	R		O	T	T		A	V	E		T	S	P
D	R	Y	A	D		E	A	T	O	N		T	W	A
			H	E	S		F	C	C		B	L	A	T
A	R	M	E	D	T	O	T	H	E	T	E	E	T	H
P	O	E	M		E	V	E		T	A	T			
S	E	N		S	P	E	R	M		R	A	I	T	A
E	S	S		A	I	R		I	F	S		C	A	T
		U	N	I	N	T	E	L	L	I	G	E	N	T
A	P	R	I	L		A	N	O	A		R	A	G	A
S	H	A	P	E		K	I	R	K		U	G	L	I
P	I	L	A	R		E	D	D	Y		B	E	E	N

48

A	C	A	R	I		D	A	F	T		P	O	S	H
L	O	W	E	R		E	S	A	U		O	L	L	A
G	R	A	D	E	S	E	P	A	R	A	T	I	O	N
A	M	I	R		M	R	S		B	U	B	O	E	S
	S	T	E	L	A			F	O	R	E			
			W	A	L	K	I	E	T	A	L	K	I	E
C	W	T		P	L	A	C	E	S		L	E	N	D
H	A	I	R			R	I	B			Y	E	T	I
O	G	L	E		O	M	E	L	E	T		L	O	T
W	E	L	S	H	R	A	R	E	B	I	T			
			P	A	D	S			B	E	S	T	S	
I	N	S	O	L	E		N	E	E		H	O	P	I
B	A	N	N	E	R	H	E	A	D	L	I	N	E	S
I	S	I	S		L	O	O	T		O	R	G	A	N
S	A	T	E		Y	E	N	S		S	T	A	R	T

Solutions

49

P	A	U	L	■	S	H	A	H	■	A	M	A	S	S
I	M	M	E	D	I	A	C	Y	■	M	A	C	H	O
L	I	B	E	R	A	T	E	D	■	E	X	C	O	N
O	R	R	■	E	M	S	■	R	A	N	■	R	A	G
T	S	A	R	S	■	■	C	A	P	I	T	A	L	S
■	■	■	O	S	I	E	R	■	E	T	H	■	■	■
T	W	O	B	Y	F	O	U	R	■	Y	E	N	T	A
O	H	I	O	■	S	N	E	E	R	■	R	A	I	D
M	O	L	T	S	■	S	L	A	C	K	E	N	E	D
■	■	■	I	T	O	■	L	L	A	N	O	■	■	■
A	R	M	C	A	N	D	Y	■	■	O	F	F	E	R
L	E	A	■	R	O	E	■	B	A	T	■	I	D	O
U	N	M	E	T	■	W	R	I	T	T	E	N	U	P
L	A	B	E	L	■	A	N	N	O	Y	A	N	C	E
A	L	O	N	E	■	R	A	S	P	■	R	Y	E	S

50

H	A	S	P	S	■	R	A	D	I	I	■	J	A	S
U	S	U	A	L	■	A	D	E	B	T	■	O	R	A
H	U	N	G	E	R	G	A	M	E	S	■	H	O	I
■	■	■	E	W	E	■	H	I	T	A	S	N	A	G
■	E	M	B	O	S	S	■	■	■	■	O	K	R	A
P	R	O	O	F	P	O	S	I	T	I	V	E	■	■
L	I	V	Y	■	■	L	A	N	A	S	■	N	R	C
O	N	I	■	S	E	D	U	C	E	R	■	N	E	A
T	S	E	■	I	R	E	N	A	■	■	B	E	I	N
■	■	S	O	B	E	R	A	S	A	J	U	D	G	E
L	E	H	R	■	■	■	■	E	V	E	L	Y	N	■
S	P	O	O	N	O	U	T	■	E	R	L	■	■	■
A	E	R	■	A	F	E	W	G	O	O	D	M	E	N
T	E	T	■	P	A	Y	E	E	■	M	O	T	T	O
S	S	S	■	A	N	S	E	L	■	E	G	A	D	S

51

H	A	B	I	T	A	T	■	I	O	C	■	S	T	P
I	S	O	L	A	T	O	■	C	A	P	S	I	Z	E
S	P	O	O	N	F	U	L	O	F	S	U	G	A	R
S	E	Z	■	■	■	S	U	N	■	N	E	H	R	U
Y	N	E	Z	■	T	L	C	■	M	O	L	T	■	■
■	■	■	E	I	R	E	■	B	O	W	■	L	V	I
M	O	R	E	S	O	■	L	E	V	■	■	E	E	C
O	N	E	■	R	I	V	U	L	E	T	■	S	N	A
P	T	L	■	■	K	E	G	■	S	I	T	S	I	N
S	O	O	■	A	A	E	■	H	U	M	E	■	■	■
■	■	C	A	L	S	■	P	E	P	■	L	A	V	S
I	M	A	R	I	■	S	O	W	■	■	■	T	O	N
S	E	T	A	G	O	O	D	E	X	A	M	P	L	E
B	R	E	N	N	A	N	■	R	I	B	C	A	G	E
N	E	S	■	S	R	O	■	S	I	E	R	R	A	S

52

L	E	A	P	■	T	I	E	D	■	I	F	O	L	D
E	L	S	E	■	R	A	N	I	■	R	A	D	I	O
W	H	I	R	L	I	N	G	D	E	R	V	I	S	H
D	I	A	L	U	P	■	S	Y	M	■	O	C	T	S
■	■	■	E	K	E	D	■	A	M	I	R	■	■	■
S	A	M	■	E	D	E	L	■	A	M	A	N	D	A
I	R	A	E	■	A	V	E	C	■	A	B	E	E	R
C	H	O	C	O	L	A	T	E	E	C	L	A	I	R
K	A	R	T	S	■	S	I	N	N	■	E	L	O	I
O	T	I	O	S	E	■	N	T	S	B	■	E	N	D
■	■	■	M	O	N	A	■	I	N	A	T	■	■	■
A	T	M	O	■	C	L	U	■	A	D	V	I	C	E
C	H	A	R	L	O	T	T	E	R	U	S	S	E	S
D	R	U	P	E	■	A	W	E	E	■	E	P	P	A
C	U	S	H	Y	■	R	O	O	S	■	T	Y	E	S

Solutions

53

A	S	T	R	A		S	T	E		F	I	R	E	D
I	L	I	E	D		N	E	Y		I	N	O	U	R
R	A	T	E	D		C	L	E	A	N	S	E	R	S
S	W	I	S	S	A	C	C	O	U	N	T			
			E	O	S		O	N	T			A	L	I
L	T	R		N	S	F			R	E	I	N	A	S
O	R	E	G		T	A	N	G	E	N	T	I	A	L
R	I	C	E	R		K	E	R		O	S	O	L	E
D	O	O	R	K	E	E	P	E	R		A	N	A	T
E	D	I	T	O	R			S	E	E		S	A	S
D	E	L			D	L	I		B	Q	E			
			B	L	O	O	D	S	A	U	S	A	G	E
L	I	K	E	I	S	A	I	D		I	S	T	L	E
I	F	E	L	L		D	O	A		T	I	M	E	R
M	A	Y	S	T		S	T	K		Y	E	S	N	O

54

A	C	I	D		S	L	A	T		R	I	G	H	T
T	E	T	E	A	T	E	T	E		O	R	R	I	S
A	N	I	T	A	L	O	O	S		S	E	E	S	A
I	T	N		H	O	N		T	A	E		T	S	R
L	O	E	S	S			A	S	H	T	R	A	Y	S
		R	O	A	R	A	T		I	T	E			
S	T	A	R	T	E	D	I	N		A	S	P	I	N
T	O	N	I		C	A	S	A	S		E	L	S	E
O	C	T	A	D		S	H	A	R	E	W	A	R	E
			N	I	S		O	N	S	P	E	C		
E	L	D	O	R	A	D	O			I	D	E	A	S
L	E	A		T	O	A		X	Y	Z		C	R	T
L	E	R	O	I		C	A	M	E	O	F	A	G	E
A	L	I	C	E		C	H	A	P	A	R	R	A	L
S	A	N	D	S		A	A	S	S		I	D	L	E

55

S	T	O	P		B	E	S	O		T	A	R	D	E
T	O	R	R		A	G	H	A		A	T	E	I	T
S	M	E	E		Y	G	O	R		S	P	A	T	S
	B	L	O	W	O	N	E	S	S	T	A	C	K	
			R	E	N	O			S	E	R	T	A	
W	E	D	D	I	N	G	B	A	N	D				
A	S	R	A	R	E		O	K	S		E	A	R	P
C	A	N	I	D		P	I	C		E	N	N	U	I
S	I	O	N		B	H	T		E	X	C	O	N	S
				M	A	D	E	A	S	P	L	A	S	H
	E	N	D	O	W			I	T	O	O			
	D	O	U	B	L	E	C	R	O	S	S	E	S	
R	E	B	E	C		C	O	I	N		U	Z	I	S
I	M	E	T	A		C	O	L	I		R	E	D	O
G	A	L	O	P		E	N	Y	A		E	K	E	S

56

L	A	H			P	A	B	A		U	D	D	E	R
E	C	O			O	N	Y	X		N	O	E	L	S
T	A	R	A		M	A	H	I		H	U	L	A	S
U	R	S	I		E	T	O	N		O	B	I	T	S
P	E	T	R	O	L		O	G	I	L	L			
			C	L	O	A	K		A	Y	E	S	I	R
A	L	G	O	L		T	O	A	N		B	U	T	A
K	A	R	M	A		T	R	L		B	A	L	E	S
I	M	A	M		S	O	B	A		U	S	U	R	P
N	A	B	O	B	S		Y	E	L	L	S			
			D	I	R	A	C		U	B	O	A	T	S
A	U	T	O	S		C	R	I	T		O	M	O	O
D	E	O	R	O		C	O	L	I		N	E	I	L
A	L	L	E	N		T	O	Y	S			S	L	A
S	E	U	S	S		S	K	A	T			S	E	R

Solutions

57

E	M	B	A	R	K		S	P	Y		O	R	T	S
B	A	I	L	E	E		O	H	O		M	E	A	T
B	O	D	I	L	Y		D	I	R	T	B	I	K	E
			T	I	P	I		L	E	A	R	N	E	R
D	O	N		C	A	C	A	O		M	E	S	O	N
A	B	E	T		D	E	I	S	M			E	N	S
M	O	V	I	E		C	R	O	P	P	E	R		
N	E	E	D	L	E	R		P	H	A	N	T	O	M
		R	E	F	R	E	S	H		P	O	I	L	U
A	S	S			R	A	P	I	D		L	O	I	N
C	H	A	S	E		M	A	Z	E	R		N	O	G
C	R	Y	P	T	I	C		E	D	I	T			
R	A	D	I	A	T	O	R		U	G	A	N	D	A
U	N	I	T		E	N	E		C	O	P	I	E	R
E	K	E	S		M	E	T		T	R	E	B	L	E

58

S	L	E	W	S			F	E	S	S		P	T	A
D	U	B	A	I		D	I	A	N	A		H	O	R
A	N	O	S	E		E	L	S	E	W	H	E	R	E
K	A	N	I	N		A	M	Y	L		Y	W	C	A
			N	A	S	T		C	L	O	D			
S	U	M	S		S	H	M	O		T	R	A	S	H
W	H	I	T	E	R	O	O	M		A	O	R	T	A
A	H	A	I	R		N	I	E		R	E	S	O	W
T	U	T	T	I		T	R	E	M	U	L	O	U	S
S	H	A	C	K		H	A	A	S		E	N	T	E
			H	A	M	E		S	N	C	C			
O	I	S	E		I	N	K	Y		E	T	A	I	L
B	R	I	S	T	L	I	N	G		I	R	I	N	A
O	E	D		R	O	L	E	O		L	I	D	O	S
E	D	S		U	S	E	E			S	C	E	N	E

59

K	E	A	N	E		G	E	O	L		S	P	A	R
E	L	R	O	Y		E	S	A	U		C	U	T	S
B	I	T	T	E		S	O	F	T	T	A	C	O	S
A	H	I		W	U	S	S		H	A	R	E	M	S
B	U	F	F	A	L	O		L	E	M	A			
		I	E	S	T		B	E	R	I	B	E	R	I
M	I	C	A	H		S	E	P	A	L		A	I	T
A	D	I	T		H	A	G	E	N		P	G	A	S
T	O	A		S	E	N	O	R		O	N	L	A	Y
A	L	L	E	Y	C	A	T		O	P	I	E		
			A	L	K	A		I	R	O	N	S	O	N
M	I	S	S	A	L		R	N	A	S		C	P	I
C	O	N	T	R	I	V	E	D		S	P	O	R	E
C	L	E	O		N	A	N	U		U	S	U	A	L
C	A	E	N		G	I	D	E		M	Y	T	H	S

60

C	T	R			M	N	E	M		R	E	B	E	L
R	E	A	M		I	O	N	A		O	V	A	T	E
E	M	M	A		A	N	N	S		W	E	G	O	T
S	P	O	R	T	S	C	A	S	T	E	R			
C	O	S	T	U	M	E			A	N	T	I	C	S
			I	P	A		T	H	R	A		T	O	I
S	H	A	N	A		H	E	A	D			I	A	L
P	A	N	I	C	A	T	T	H	E	D	I	S	C	O
A	D	D			X	M	E	N		O	M	I	T	S
R	T	E		A	I	L	S		A	Y	S			
K	O	S	O	V	O			S	T	O	O	D	O	N
			H	U	M	P	T	Y	D	U	M	P	T	Y
V	I	N	Y	L		R	O	S	A		A	L	O	E
O	B	I	E	S		I	N	O	W		D	U	E	T
C	O	P	S	E		E	S	P	N			S	S	S

Solutions

61

O	L	D	E		A	G	E	D			B	T	E	N
T	R	A	N	S	P	O	S	E	S		B	E	L	S
H	O	R	R	E	N	D	O	U	S		B	E	B	E
E	N	C	O	R	E		S	C	T	V		T	O	C
			U	T	A	H		E	S	C	R	O	W	
E	V	I	T	A		A	A	S		H	E	T		
T	O	N	E		I	T	S		V	I	V	A	C	E
A	L	F		S	C	H	L	E	P	P		L	A	A
S	T	I	F	L	E		I	V	S		S	E	T	S
		E	L	A		A	P	E		T	U	R	V	Y
	S	L	O	C	U	M		S	O	I	R			
T	I	D		K	N	E	W		R	E	P	A	I	R
H	E	F	T		C	L	A	R	K	G	A	B	L	E
I	N	L	A		S	I	D	E	I	S	S	U	E	S
S	A	Y	S			A	E	O	N		S	T	A	T

62

S	I	S	I		O	C	A	L	A		M	A	A	S
E	C	U	S		C	O	M	I	C		I	D	L	Y
P	A	P	E	R	C	H	A	S	E		S	V	E	N
T	H	E	R	U	L	E	S		T	U	T	E	E	S
A	N	S		N	U	N		H	O	N	O	R		
			I	T	D		L	U	L	L		S	V	U
P	E	C	S		E	M	I	R		A	N	A	I	S
A	T	A	L	O	S	S	F	O	R	W	O	R	D	S
G	A	N	E	F		D	E	K	E		I	Y	A	R
O	S	T		T	S	O	S		N	I	L			
		O	B	E	Y	S		S	A	T		B	B	A
S	A	N	D	A	L		S	T	U	B	B	O	R	N
S	H	E	A		P	U	R	P	L	E	R	A	I	N
N	O	S	Y		H	I	T	A	T		E	S	T	A
S	T	E	S		S	E	A	T	S		A	T	T	S

63

M	P	A	A		H	I	D	E		O	D	I	U	M
D	I	C	K		E	N	O	L		M	I	N	T	Y
S	P	E	C	I	A	L	T	Y		E	N	D	U	P
E	E	S		R	D	A	S				E	I	R	E
			A	R	O	W		H	Y	D	R	A	N	T
M	A	S	L	I	N		C	A	M	E	O	N		
G	R	I	E	G		A	L	O	H	A		C	G	I
M	I	S	C	A	L	C	U	L	A	T	I	O	N	S
T	A	B		T	E	H	E	E		H	O	R	A	L
		O	P	E	N	E	D		S	T	U	N	T	S
T	A	O	I	S	T	S		T	O	R	S			
A	C	M	E				P	I	S	A		M	K	T
L	I	B	R	E		H	O	M	O	P	H	O	N	E
I	D	A	R	E		C	L	E	O		A	N	O	N
A	S	H	E	N		H	I	S	N		S	A	T	S

64

O	R	S	E	R		S	P	E	S		S	A	S	E
L	E	M	M	A		H	U	L	A		A	C	T	A
A	B	E	A	T		E	N	V	Y		L	E	O	V
Y	A	W	N	E	R		Y	E	S	M		I	V	E
			U	D	A	Y		S	H	U	N	N	E	D
H	I	B	E	R	N	I	A		I	M	S			
T	O	O	L		T	E	R	R		M	C	R	I	B
T	W	A			S	L	E	E	K			I	N	A
P	A	R	K	E		D	S	M	S		O	A	T	H
			O	S	O		O	U	T	S	M	A	R	T
R	I	S	O	T	T	O		S	A	K	E			
I	V	O		H	I	R	E		R	O	L	L	E	D
C	I	N	C		O	I	L	S		K	E	E	L	S
E	E	E	S		S	Y	M	S		I	T	A	L	O
R	S	S	S		E	A	S	T		E	S	P	Y	S

Solutions

65

L	U	L	U			R	H	O	S		E	N	Y	A
I	H	O	P		P	A	A	V	O		L	E	E	R
N	O	S	H		U	N	R	E	P		E	R	L	E
C	H	E	E	S	E	I	T	T	H	E	C	O	P	S
			R	A	R			T	I	P	T			
A	S	C	E	T	I	C			A	R	I	S	E	
I	L	A			L	O	D	E		O	O	H	S	
D	O	U	B	L	E	I	N	D	E	M	N	I	T	Y
	E	S	A	I		L	Y	N	N			R	E	O
	S	E	D	E	R			A	D	O	P	T	E	D
			A	G	E	E			L	D	L			
D	A	N	C	E	D	A	N	C	E	D	A	N	C	E
A	L	O	T		S	T	Y	E	S		N	O	O	R
I	D	I	O		E	U	R	O	S		O	M	E	N
S	A	D	R		A	P	O	S			N	O	D	S

66

S	A	L	V	O			A	D	D		A	N	O	N
A	L	I	E	N		N	C	I	S		L	I	N	A
M	A	K	E	T	R	A	C	K	S		O	C	H	S
E	D	E		A	A	A				S	M	O	O	T
			S	P	E	C	I	F	I	C	A	L	L	Y
A	M	A	H			P	R	E	P	A	R	E	D	
P	E	R	U	S	E		O	N	A	N				
I	N	F	I	T	S	A	N	D	S	T	A	R	T	S
				I	S	T	O		S	Y	N	O	D	S
	S	P	A	N	I	A	R	D			C	E	S	T
U	N	R	E	G	E	N	E	R	A	T	E			
D	A	I	R	Y				A	R	I		A	R	O
D	I	D	I		B	E	I	N	N	E	E	D	O	F
E	L	E	E		Y	O	L	K		O	N	I	O	N
R	S	S	S		S	E	E			N	O	T	S	O

67

W	I	D	E		G	U	L	A	G		A	C	L	U
A	R	O	D		A	P	O	L	O		M	I	E	N
T	O	N	Y		M	O	U	T	H	G	U	A	R	D
U	N	A		T	E	N		I	O	U	S			
S	O	L	D	E	R	E	R		M	Y	T	Y	P	E
I	N	D	E	X			I	R	E	S		A	R	Y
			B	A	H	R	A	I	N		I	L	I	E
T	O	O	T	S	I	E		G	O	A	T	E	E	D
A	M	P	S		M	O	H	A	W	K	S			
N	N	E		C	A	S	A			I	N	I	G	O
H	I	L	L	E	L		P	I	A	N	O	B	A	R
			A	C	A	I		S	I	S		E	S	T
H	O	C	K	E	Y	M	A	S	K		A	R	M	E
B	A	U	M		A	T	R	E	E		D	I	A	G
O	R	L	E		N	O	T	I	N		U	S	N	A

68

G	O	N	G	S		T	A	B	U		S	C	A	B
S	P	I	R	Y		R	U	I	N		A	L	G	A
A	E	S	O	P		A	R	T	S		L	E	I	S
	N	I	G	H	T	W	A	T	C	H	M	A	N	
				O	I	L			R	A	I	N		
O	C	T	A	N	E		L	Y	E	S		S	A	C
P	A	Y	P	E	R	V	I	E	W		B	L	U	R
T	I	R	E	D		E	S	T		P	R	A	D	O
E	R	A	S		A	N	T	I	B	I	O	T	I	C
D	O	N		A	N	D	S		I	N	S	E	T	S
		N	A	V	Y			G	N	P				
	C	I	N	E	M	A	T	O	G	R	A	P	H	
L	O	C	I		O	R	A	L		I	G	L	O	O
E	X	A	M		R	I	F	F		C	H	U	M	P
K	A	L	E		E	A	T	S		K	A	M	E	S

Solutions

69

U	S	S	R	■	A	T	M	S	■	T	A	B	L	E
R	O	C	A	■	L	E	O	I	■	A	X	I	A	L
B	A	R	T	■	I	R	O	N	■	L	E	W	I	S
A	M	A	T	■	I	M	M	A	C	U	L	A	T	E
N	I	P	U	P	■	I	O	T	A	S	■	■	■	■
■	■	P	S	I	■	N	O	R	N	■	P	F	C	S
E	S	A	■	S	R	I	■	A	D	M	I	R	E	S
P	E	P	I	T	A	■	■	■	I	R	K	I	N	G
P	R	E	T	E	N	D	■	H	D	L	■	G	S	T
S	T	R	S	■	L	U	R	E	■	E	P	H	■	■
■	■	■	■	S	O	B	E	R	■	E	A	T	O	N
B	L	A	C	K	W	I	D	O	W	■	S	W	A	T
R	A	L	L	Y	■	O	D	I	E	■	S	I	T	E
O	N	E	U	P	■	U	L	N	A	■	U	G	H	S
S	A	R	E	E	■	S	E	E	K	■	P	S	S	T